O.N.U.

Dept Education

FOR SPEECH CORRECTION AND SPEECH IMPROVEMENT

Louise Binder Scott
Associate Professor of Speech Education
Los Angeles State College
Los Angeles, California
and
J. J. Thompson
Associate Professor of Speech
Long Beach State College
Long Beach, California

WEBSTER PUBLISHING COMPANY
St. Louis • Atlanta • Dallas • Pasadena

FOREWORD

The greatest number of speech problems in school children involve articulatory substitutions, omissions, or sound distortions. When these deficiencies are not caused by organic conditions, they are simply functional habits of faulty sound discriminations caused by imitation, training, or conflicts in early speech production. These faults can be very easily corrected, in most cases, without severe speech correction procedures, by using indirect methods of speech improvement conducted by classroom teachers in the regular learning processes of an integrated school program.

But classroom teachers who have had no training in speech or its deviations ask the question, "How is this done?"

In answer to this question, TALKING TIME presents methods and materials which have been tried and tested successfully in the Pasadena and San Marino City Schools of California. The authors have demonstrated the efficacy of speech games, exercises, poems, and stories in pleasant speaking experiences for children of the elementary grades.

It has been my personal pleasure to observe the authors doing speech correction and speech improvement in their respective schools and demonstrating for my teachers in training at the University of Southern California. Results have been gratifying and convincing. In the use of these carefully selected materials, children are not made to feel conspicuous or self-conscious because of speech errors, such as the formal frontal attack is bound to create. Speech timidities, psychological blockages, anxieties, and tensions can be resolved in a dynamic speech program such as TALKING TIME presents. Classroom teachers and parents will find the proper use of this book good assurance toward more effective communication.

CONRAD F. WEDBERG
Field Representative in Speech Correction
State Department of Education
Sacramento, California

INTRODUCTION

"Speech correction should be a part of, not apart from, the everyday experiences of the child."

TALKING TIME is an outgrowth of the realization of the need for a simple, non-technical book that will aid in the correction of sound substitutions and in the improvement of speech difficulties in all children. The book has been arranged so that classroom teachers can easily locate the areas in which speech problems exist and make use of the poems, stories, and devices which will provide practice on the sound or sounds which may be defective. The consistent use of repetitive drills in the most commonly defective sounds will soon show results in a child's speech pattern.

The authors have tried to appeal to humor and imagination within the field of experiences of primary children in order to help them to become pleasantly speech conscious without becoming emotionally speech self-conscious. The material is designed to give practice in feeling kinesthetically and in hearing the correct sound patterns.

There is little value in dwelling upon isolated sound elements beyond the point of correct production because there is no practicality in continued drill on sounds except as they fit into words and sentences. Drill through play will pave the way toward mastery of the most frequently defective elements in speech.

The primary level is the logical place to begin speech training in school. Here is awakened the desire to talk and to share orally one's experiences. Here the teacher can take steps to correct faulty speech habits before they become more firmly imbedded. If an incorrect speech habit is allowed to persist, the process of re-education is not only that of creating a new speech pattern, but also that of erasing the old one. A great deal of effective speech training can be done at this level, since self-consciousness has not yet arisen to hinder the child in his expression.

The authors subscribe to the philosophy that the group situation which the classroom provides is the ideal place to correct many of the speech and speech-emotional problems of children. While it is sometimes necessary to give a child individual assistance or the help which a speech clinic group provides, it is felt that all too frequently the problem of the child is amplified when he is segregated from the regular classroom routine for special instruction.

The authors have experienced personally many situations wherein a child overcame his speech problem in the classroom without being aware that he had a problem through the use of such speech games and devices as are included in TALKING TIME. These speech problems were of so serious a nature that the correction could not be ascribed solely to maturation.

In a classroom where there is an understanding teacher, speech activities can become so integrated into the daily classroom routine that no child need be aware that he is being singled out as deviating from so-called normal speech patterns. The entire class will accept the responsibility of improving each other's speech, and the teacher soon notices that there is no teasing a child with a speech handicap. Instead, there is an earnest endeavor on the part of all the children to restore the speech-handicapped child to the standards which the group has set for itself under the guidance of the teacher.

It must be recognized by teachers and parents that there are many speech problems which are really emotional problems expressed through the speech mechanism.

In such instances, the teacher and the parent should seek out competent professional advice from a speech therapist or psychologist before attempting direct or indirect therapy on the child's speech. In all cases of speech deviations, the parents should be brought into the picture in order to continue the speech drills, in a play way, in the atmosphere of the home. In those cases in which the problem is basically an emotional one expressing itself through speech, it is the parents, and not the children, who will need the guidance and counseling which the professional can provide. The teacher herself can capitalize, however, upon the advantages of the group situation of the classroom in building emotional stability and security in the speech-emotionally-handicapped child.

Such practice as TALKING TIME affords, the authors hope, will help children to take a delight in speech generally and in their own specifically.

L. B. SCOTT

J. J. THOMPSON

ACKNOWLEDGMENTS

The authors express their thanks for the use of the following materials: "Little Jack Pumpkin Face" and "See the Windmill Turning" from *The First Grade Book of Our Singing World,* copyrighted, 1949, by permission of Ginn and Company; "This Is the Gate the Steam Comes Through" from *The Rehabilitation of Speech,* Revised Edition, 1947, West, Kennedy, and Carr, by permission of Harper and Brothers and Miss Anna Carr; "Five Little Kittens," permission of *The Grade Teacher;* The University Society Publishers for permission to adapt and use finger play exercises; "The Clock," "Mr. Clock," and "Christmas Bells" from *Sounds for Little Folks* and "Easter Rabbits" and "The Choo Choo Train" from *Speech Improvement Through Choral Speaking,* permission of Expression Company; "Fuzzy Wuzzy," permission of Conrad F. Wedberg; "My Tongue," permission of Miss Frances C. Hunte, Speech Development Teacher, Garvey School District, Garvey, California.

Gratitude is extended to Mrs. Verna Breinholt, Speech Consultant, Orange County Schools, California, for serving as an adviser for the sections on relaxation and group speaking; and to Mr. Conrad F. Wedberg, Field Representative in Speech Correction, California State Department of Education, for writing the foreword.

THE CONTENTS

PART II—Continued

PART III

PART I

HOW TO USE THIS BOOK

Every teacher is a teacher of speech, either consciously or unconsciously, for the speech habits and the speech development of a child are affected and influenced by the activities that take place in the classroom.

TALKING TIME provides the teacher of primary children with informal materials which are designed to improve or correct a child's speech pattern. You, as a teacher, will find that the materials in TALKING TIME can be incorporated into what you are already doing and that speech education need not involve a special time set aside from the regular reading, language arts, social science, or phonics periods. The authors assume that all teachers on primary levels have had some practice with sounds along with their training in the teaching of reading skills.

You are undoubtedly aware that there are speech problems in your room. A child's speech may deviate from the normal pattern. He just does not talk like the other children. Perhaps he hesitates, stutters, or blocks when attempting to communicate. In that case, calling attention to his speech mechanism through speech drills will not help. *He talks the way he talks because he feels the way he feels* and his case should be referred to a speech spe-

1

cialist or a psychologist. However, if a child distorts or omits sounds, you can do something about it. TALKING TIME will help you to determine the substitutions a child is making and will tell you how to cope with the problem.

Later in this chapter the procedure in making a speech survey is explained. Through this simplified checking device you may uncover the impediments in the speech of your children. Knowing which sounds are defective, you can then turn to the section in this book which deals with the sound or sounds presenting difficulty. Practice with a mirror so that you will be able to explain to the child what he should do. Check your own tongue movements. Discover what your lips and teeth do when the sound is made. Feel your voice box to see whether or not it vibrates.

You are also given suggestions for correcting the sound and a name to call it. It means much more to the child when the sound is given a name that ties into his own experiences. Young children do not know the sound by its letter designation, such as the S sound or the CH sound, but if you tell them about the sound the snake makes, "s...s...s...," or the train sound, "ch...ch ...ch," or the hair clippers sound, "zh...zh...zh," they will comprehend and listen for that sound in their own speech and in the speech of others.

The consonant sounds of speech appear in this book as small letters in quotation marks. Unless otherwise stated, these sounds are to be pronounced as they would be in a word, not as letters of the alphabet. The sound of "s" is to be said as the initial sound of *say*, not as *ess*.

The word lists in each sound section are for your own

2

information. The sound is used in the initial, medial, and final positions. You will want to find as many pictures as possible of the noun words in order to use them in the speech survey or in the speech games included in the sound sections.

The poems or jingles usually have refrains which are designed to produce the sound that is wanted. However, you should first explain to the children what they are to do and then show them the correct way of doing it. Ask them to listen for the certain sound upon which you are drilling. Take the positive approach . . . "Let us do this." Avoid asking "Would you like to do this?" Children are often not sure what is expected of them and they may surprise you by answering "No."

Speech education needs to be approached in a matter-of-fact way. Praise and patience are two vitally important factors. When exasperation or impatience on the part of the teacher or the child enters into the picture, stop . . . take a break . . . change activity for awhile. A child who is unable to make a sound correctly after repeated efforts should still be praised for his attempts. Be very sure that when he is able to produce the sound successfully he is given a chance to demonstrate his ability for others. He should be given recognition as soon as possible by allowing him to get up in front of the group and make the sound for the other children. He must feel that he is accepted by the teacher and the group in spite of his speech.

A child with a severe speech problem often needs special help outside the group. This help should be given daily in five or ten minute periods which will be far more effective than a half hour once or twice a week.

3

A speech survey should take place early in each school year in order to discover those functional sound substitutions and other speech problems that may be present among the children. Once the class has been surveyed and the speech deviations have been classified, the teacher can then plan her program for integrating speech into the course of study. Many of the games and devices in this book can be used for reading readiness, either with groups or as seat work. An index for unit integration included at the back of the book will serve as a time saver for a busy teacher. The poetry and stories can be used to enrich the language arts program. They tie in readily with units on the farm, the circus, transportation, etc. The poems and jingles are written for unison speaking with the children giving the refrains. However, the children will soon learn all of the lines through frequent repetitions.

Precede any speech-improvement activities with an adequate preparation step. Tell the children that they are going to learn about their speech helpers, the teeth, tongue, lips, nose, voice box, and the hard and soft palates. The word "palate" will take on meaning when the child is asked to feel the hard and soft parts of the roof of his mouth with his tongue. Tell the children about the sounds they use when they speak. Explain how each sound is made as the children are exposed to it. Demonstrate carefully. If mirrors are available, let the children use them. Make sure that any child who has difficulty in making the sound being discussed gets a chance to hear and see it made correctly. Vibrations of many of the sounds ("m," "n," "ng," "v," "z," etc.) can

4

be felt on the nose, the cheeks, the lips, or the voice box. Let the children feel these vibrations on your face and throat as you make the sound. Have them feel the vibrations on their own faces and throats.

Integrate speech so thoroughly into the daily program that it becomes a definite part of each learning activity. Children should learn to expect it as the usual rather than the unusual. It should not call attention to itself as speech for the sake of speech, but speech as a means of improving one's ability to communicate adequately with other persons.

A child with a speech problem may show feelings of inadequacy, resentment, antagonism, or other emotional involvements. It is useless to proceed with the speech education of such a child until the cause for the behavior has been alleviated and the environment has been adjusted. Speech deviations may be symptoms of a child's feelings about himself and the people and factors in his surroundings. Attempts to "bombard" a child with speech drills may only amplify the symptom and make it more difficult to eliminate. The child should be kept within the classroom group as much as possible in order to avoid being singled out as "different" from the other boys and girls.

The poems and stories in TALKING TIME have been written to provide fun, enjoyment, and feelings of pleasure in speech situations as well as to provide drill and repetitious exercises for speech improvement. Use them in that light. Help the child to look forward to his speech experiences as periods in which every child can achieve his own measure of success and satisfaction.

The speech survey is a means of determining the sound or sounds which are defective, misarticulated, misplaced, or omitted in a child's speech.

A very simple survey technique is to have the child count to twelve or name the different colors. Most of the sounds that present difficulty are contained in numbers and colors.

one	—"w," "n"	red	—"r," "d"
two	—"t"	blue	—"b," "l"
three	—"th" (voiceless), "r"	green	—"g," "r"
four	—"f," "r"	yellow	—"y," "l"
five	—"f," "v"	pink	—"p," "ng," "k"
six	—"s," "ks"	black	—"b," "l," "k"
seven	—"s," "v," "n"	purple	—"r," "l"
eight	—"t"	brown	—"r"
nine	—"n"	orange	—"r," "j"
ten	—"t," "n"	white	—"wh," "t"
eleven	—"l," "v," "n"	gray	—"g," "r"
twelve	—"w," "l," "v"	silver	—"s," "l," "r"

The "ch" and "sh" sounds may be checked by having the child say: "I choose the red color" or "I will show you the green color."

Small colored paper squares, circles, or ribbons will aid in getting the child to say the color. Miniature objects are excellent for testing sounds. A child will take great delight in reaching into a "surprise" box and telling the teacher that he has taken out a spoon ("s") or a telephone ("f") or a ring ("r").

Comprehensive tests can be prepared by using the

word lists under each sound section. Find objects or pictures that match the words. Classify them, according to sound, as initial, medial, and final. This type of test should be used for children who appear to have a number of sound problems as revealed by the color and number test.

DEVICES TO USE WITH THIS BOOK

The devices explained in this section are designed for many of the speech activities in this book. The instructions to the teacher which accompany the poems, games, and stories may refer to one of the devices listed here. If so, the teacher should turn to this section for an explanation of how to make it, either as a visual aid for her own use, or as a pattern for the children to copy.

To Make a Magic Flannel Board

Select a piece of heavy cardboard or plywood, about 2 x 3 feet, depending upon the degree of portability desired. Cover this with outing flannel, suede, or sandpaper. Flannel is preferred since it can be more easily colored or painted to represent a scene. Flannel that has a fuzzy nap will give the best adhering qualities. Paste small pieces of flannel on the back of any picture which is to be used on the board. Press the pictures under a heavy weight to avoid curling edges.

To Make Paper Bag Puppets

Any paper sack or bag of the kind available in a grocery store may be used; the smaller sizes are easier to manipulate and control. Use the bag with the bottom folded down in the position in which such bags are usually stacked.

The bag can take the form of any animal or human figure, except that certain animals with long snouts or trunks will require more ingenuity in construction. Cut off the head of the figure so that the chin and lower lip are still fastened to the body. The head portion, which contains all those features down to, and including, the upper lip, is pasted on the folded bottom of the bag. The rest of the figure is pasted on the side of the bag so that the lower lip comes just below the folded bottom, and in contact with the head portion. Paint the area inside this folded bottom to resemble the inside of a mouth. Teeth and tongue can be drawn in also. The child places his hand inside the bag so that the fingers can bend into the folded flap. The movements of the fingers as they bend up and down will give the impression that the mouth of the puppet is moving as in speech.

To Make Stick Puppets

These are even easier to make than paper bag puppets. Simply cut out the figures desired, back them with cardboard, and staple or thumbtack them to small dowel sticks. If used on a hand puppet stage, the sticks are always kept out of sight. "The Little Red Hen" and "Three Billy Goats Gruff" are excellent stories to tell through the use of stick puppets.

To Make Finger Ring Puppets

Cut a strip of paper ¾ inch wide and long enough to be fastened into a ring that will fit the finger tip. Trace an outline of the object or the head of the bird or animal called for in the poem or story on another piece of paper and color it. Cut it out and paste it on the finger ring.

Scotch tape may be used instead of paste. Make as many finger rings as are needed for the rhyme. Many of the poems included in the section on "Finger Play" can be told with finger ring puppets. For example, in "The Five Little Squirrels," the child removes a squirrel head finger ring as he says each line. His hands are then free to clap together on the word *bang*.

To Make a Fishing Game

In the "sh" unit there is a poem entitled "Fishing" which calls for a fishing game. Cut out fishes about six inches long from cardboard. On each fish write one or two words containing the "sh" sound, or any other sound upon which the children need drill. Place a paper clip on the head of each fish. Tie a magnet on one end of a piece of string and on the other end tie a short stick to represent a fishing pole. The child holds the pole and dips the magnet into a cardboard pool or a fish bowl. The paper clips are attracted to the magnet so that the child may pull out a fish on the end of his line.

To Make Sleepy Toys

Secure patterns for stuffed animals and dolls. Cut them out of cloth and stuff them with lamb's wool or kapok so that they will be soft to the touch and give a relaxed, almost floppy appearance. Embroider closed eyes with lashes to indicate sleep. Check the section on "Relaxation" for poems and stories with which these are to be used.

To Make a Birthday Cake

Cut a circle of paper to form the top of the cake and a four-inch paper strip to form the sides. Fasten the strip into a circle and scotch-tape the round top to it. At the base of the cake cut slits which can be bent back and glued to a square standard that has been covered with colored paper. Paste white or pink crepe paper over the cake for frosting. Glue on birthday decorations and enough candle holders so that the cake can be used for any primary-age child. Insert candles as they are needed. Check the section on the "wh" sound for poems with which to use the birthday cake.

To Make a Pinwheel

Take a six-inch square of colored paper. Cut in from each corner to within an inch of the center. Take every other point thus cut and fasten it with a thumb tack to the head of a pencil. The points should be fastened loosely enough so that the pinwheel will spin when blown. This device is referred to in the section on the "wh" sound.

To Make a "Speech Sounds" Toy Collection

In most ten-cent or variety stores there are small inexpensive toys that are very helpful in getting a child to make certain sounds. These include doll furniture, miniature tools and utensils, toy animals and vehicles. Label a box for each of the sounds and place within it all of the objects containing that sound in either the initial, medial, or final position. The "s" box may contain a horse, saw, salt shaker, basket, and spoon. In the "r" box may be found a rooster, hammer, rabbit, fork, and airplane.

The sound boxes may be used with many of the games mentioned under the various sound sections.

To Make a "Speech Sounds" Picture Collection

Collect pictures which will illustrate the individual

poems and games contained in this book. For example, in the section on the "r" sound, find a picture of a rooster crowing for the poem, "Rooster"; a lion in a zoo for the poem, "Lion"; children playing in the rain for the poem, "Raindrops."

All pictures should be large enough so that the children in the back of the room can see them. The pictures should not contain too many objects, and the background or mounting should be attractive and contrasting, but should not detract from the picture.

To Make a Standard for Ice Cream Cones

Two smooth boards about 9x18 inches are needed. In one of them drill holes 1¼ inches in diameter so that cones placed into them will remain upright. A four-inch dowel should be nailed to each corner of this board. When the second board is fastened to these dowels. there will be a space between the two boards wide enough so that the ends of the cones will not touch the base of the standard. This device is used with "The Party" game in the section on the "s" sound.

UNISON SPEAKING

Much of the material in this book makes use of a technique known variously as verse choir, voice choir, group speaking, or as the authors prefer to call it, unison speaking. Experience has shown this to be one of the most valuable techniques in the field of speech improvement and speech correction.

The technique is not new. Tribal groups in ancient times chanted in unison. Primitive tribes today still carry on unison speaking in their festivals and ceremonials.

11

Early Greek playwrights used the chorus to set the scene and establish moods. This device can be traced down through history in religious ceremonies and the pageantry of the drama to the responsive readings of the minister and congregation in our present-day churches.

As recently as a decade ago, the use of unison speaking in education was practically unknown except for its entertainment value. Now educators are beginning to realize that unison speaking can be used as a means for alleviating emotional problems as well as for improving and correcting speech.

The child handicapped by baby talk, the stutterer, the child with delayed speech, the child from a home where foreign language is spoken, all are aided in overcoming a difficult handicap that may prevent a satisfactory school life. By learning to become a part of the whole, by submerging one's personality into the personality of the group, the child can gain a feeling of belongingness and security and a sense of achievement. The opportunity to speak in unison enables the child to develop poise and confidence in himself. Thus released, he is better equipped for solo work, either with the group or in the sharing activities of the classroom.

Unison speaking can be used as a device for achieving relaxation by proper selection of verse which emphasizes or permits bodily movement and rhythm.

It invites creative ability with free expression of imagination. One of the obvious benefits from this type of speaking is the teamwork it engenders, since the child is dependent on others for the success of the end result.

In relating unison speaking to speech improvement, proper selection of poetry again will provide a constant repetition of certain sounds, which if correctly made will help the child to establish the right patterns of speech. He will establish, also, a feeling of the sound with his tongue, teeth, and lips, so that the various senses are brought into play at the same time ... hearing, touch, speech, and the kinesthetic muscle sense.

RELAXATION

Present-day living too often calls for great expenditures of nervous energy. Children find that their store of energy is being rapidly depleted early in each day. The increased physical and mental tensions that are built up as a result work themselves out as behavior problems and emotional sprees. The teacher should seek out every technique available to make children in her classroom mindful of energy conservation. She should try to instill within them the ability to relax, if only momentarily, in order to revitalize the body mechanism.

The term *relaxation* does not imply that a person must lie flat on his back or slump in a chair, letting his mind go blank. In fact, some children find this impossible to do. If they try to relax, they immediately become rigid and tense. They need more tangible techniques to accomplish this physical and mental stillness.

A number of books have been written containing excellent advice on how to recognize the symptoms of nervous tension. An alert teacher can spot symptoms of such tensions before they develop into untoward behavior.

The following pages contain many techniques which a teacher can use in preserving the emotional stability of her classroom. For example, the class may take time out

for a game of "rag doll." The teacher asks the children to pretend that they are limp like a rag doll; no bones at all. Upon seeing a relaxed-looking doll, the children take on the feeling and respond with limpness. During these periods, it is imperative that the teacher relax, too. It is she who sets the tempo of the room and it is she who transmits her feelings of tension or calmness to the children.

Relaxation should be a play activity, a natural follow-up of recess time or a prolonged seat-work period. Stories, poems, sleepy toys, and games are a few of the devices that can be used to create stillness. A few minutes spent on a "still" time when the children come in from recess, after lunch, or following concentrated work, will do wonders in relieving emotional tensions. Learning processes will certainly be improved.

Frequent and short periods of relaxation will achieve best results. One should not wait until he is completely exhausted, but should recharge his mental batteries frequently by reminding himself to keep relaxed.

14

The section which follows will provide poems, games, stories, and other suggestions which the teacher may use for a period of physical or mental stillness.

STILL TIME

I've just come in from playing.
I'm as tired as I can be.
I'll cross my legs
And fold my hands
And close my eyes so I can't see.
I will not move my body;
I'll be like Raggedy Ann.
My head won't move;
My arms won't move.
I'll just be still,
Because I CAN.

Read the poem, pausing at the end of each line to see that children follow instructions, after first demonstrating what to do. This is a projected type of relaxation.

QUIET TIME

When I have my quiet time,
I walk to sleepy hill
And climb up to the very top
Where everything is still.

The darkness wraps its blanket
Around me, and down deep
I sink into my pillow,
And soon I'm fast asleep.

Read slowly with frequent pauses. At the close of the reading, mention names of certain children who have been "quiet" listeners.

HUSH

Hush . . . sh . . . everybody, please;
Not a speck of noise.
Tiptoe very quietly;
We're through with playing toys.
Hush . . . sh . . . everybody, please;
Not a single peep.
Let's drop our heads and close our eyes.
Pretend we're fast asleep.

Alternate last lines may be used.

I'm covering up my kitty,
And now she's fast asleep.

Substitute any toy which a child might choose. Say this poem as the
children come in from play to take their seats.

16

SNOWFLAKES

Teacher: Pretend snowflakes are falling...
Children: Down ... down ... down ...
Teacher: There must be snow for Santa's sleigh,
    Or he will never find the way.
Children: Down ... down ... down ...
Teacher: Sh ... sh ... it is so very still.
    I hear upon the window sill,
    All through the night, all through the day,
    Soft white snowflakes there at play.
    Pretend snowflakes are falling ...
Children: Down ... down ... down ...

 Children say the refrain as indicated, letting the hands drop slowly into their laps from overhead, fingers moving lightly to imitate snowflakes. Children's voices descend in pitch as they say the refrain.

The Waterfall

 The teacher plays "By the Waters of Minnetonka" as the children imitate a waterfall, saying: "Hush, hush, hush, hush," in rhythm to the music. If *hush* is said softly, the effect will sound like rushing water. This device is excellent for producing the "sh" sound.

 Rush may be substituted for *hush,* thus getting drill on the "r" sound.

17

SOFT THINGS

Teacher: Can you think of something that is soft? (Wait for answers.) Close your eyes. I have my eyes closed and I can see a baby chick. Try to see it, too. Tell me something soft that you can see ... Perhaps you can see a fluffy kitty. What does the kitty say when she is relaxed? ... I will say a poem for you. Listen carefully and when I am finished, you will know what the kitty, the puppy, the duckling, and the chickens say.

Teacher: Little fluffy kitten,
           Soft, soft fur;
           Stroke it gently, it will say,
Children: "Purr, purr, purr."
Teacher: Little woolly puppy dog,
           Soft, not rough;
           Stroke it gently, it will say,
Children: "Wuff, wuff, wuff."
Teacher: Little downy chicken,
           Cuddled down asleep;
           Stroke it gently, it will say,
Children: "Peep, peep, peep."
Teacher: Little yellow duckling,
           Soft velvet back;
           Stroke it gently, it will say,
Children: "Quack, quack, quack."

Pictures may be held up to illustrate soft things. The idea is to get a projected feeling of quiet and to establish comfort in the nervous child.

Birthday Candle Exercise

Let us pretend that we are candles on a cake. You may choose which color you like. First we stand up tall and straight. We look just like wooden soldiers. Our bodies are stiff like the candles. Now the sun is coming out very warm. You begin to melt. First your head droops ... then your shoulders ... then your arms ... your wax is melting slowly. Your legs droop ... slowly ... slowly ... until you are all melted into a puddle of wax on the floor. Now a cold wind comes along and it blows "wh ... wh ... wh ..." as you stand up straight and tall again.

This exercise teaches body control. Many children will not be able to sink to the floor gradually, but if repeated, the exercise will improve the coordination. Talking slowly in a soft voice will help the children to get the feeling of relaxation.

READINESS

Close your eyes, head drops down,
Face is smooth, not a frown.
Roll to left; head is a ball;
Roll to right; now sit tall.
Lift your chin, look at me;
Deep, deep breath, one, two, three.
Big, big smile; hands in lap.
Make believe you've had a nap.
Now you're rested from your play;
Time to work again today.

Sleepy Toy Game

Use sleepy toys: Sleepy Monkey, Sleepy Sam, Rag Doll, or Snoozy Puppy. Show the children how limp the toy can be. Ask them to pretend they have no bones in their bodies. The following jingle can be sung or recited:

> Sleepy Brown Monkey is very limp,
> Very limp, very limp;
> Sleepy Brown Monkey is very limp,
> And I can be limp, too.

The child will enjoy coming to the front of the class and showing the rest of the children how to be limp. A name may be substituted for the toy as the verse is recited or sung.

SLEEPY TIME

Teacher: My daddy and my mummy
Came to watch me sleep.
They tiptoed softly up the stairs,
As still as they could creep.

Children: Sh . . . sh . . . still.

Teacher: They whispered by my bedside,
And looked at me awhile;
I had my eyes shut tightly,
But I could feel them smile.

Children: Sh . . . sh . . . still.

Teacher: I did not move a bit and lay
As quiet as I could keep,
Because I knew they wanted me
To be so sound asleep.

Children: Sh . . . sh . . . still.

A picture of a sleeping child can be used as a preparation step. The refrain by the children may be entirely whispered. The teacher should substitute her own name in place of daddy and mummy to emphasize the fact that she, too, wants the children to pretend they are fast asleep.

RESTING TIME

And now recess is over.
Your playing time is done.
Your feet are still, your hands are still.
I'm watching everyone
To see if arms and necks are limp.
With shoulders drooping low,
Your head is resting in your arms,
As off to sleep you go.

As the teacher reads the poem, the children follow instructions. The teacher should feel the arms and the shoulders to see if they are limp. Comments may be made: "Jane's arms are limp," "Dick feels still."

SLEEPY THINGS

I like to love my Sleepy Sam;
I like to hug him, too;
I like to go to bed with him
And sleep the whole night through.

Substitute other sleepy toys, letting the children take turns holding them while the poem is said by the class. In the last line, the children should close their eyes, drop their heads, and pretend to sleep.

RAGGEDY ANN

Raggedy Ann is my best friend.
She's so relaxed; just see her bend.
First at the waist, then at the knee.
Her arms are swinging, oh, so free.
Her head rolls around like a rubber ball.
She hasn't any bones at all.
Raggedy Ann is stuffed with rags;
That's why her body wigs and wags.

Show a Raggedy Ann doll to the children before the poem is said. Ask them to pretend that they are stuffed with rags and to imitate the Raggedy Ann in the poem, doing what she does.

SCARECROW

Flip, flop, flip, flop,
See the scarecrow go
Flip, flop, flip, flop.
Bending to and fro,
To the left, to the right,
Back and forth with all his might;
Then the wind is quiet and so . . .
Flip, flop, flop, *(slowly)*
Flip, flop, flop, *(very slowly)*
Flop!

YAWNING

I yawn and yawn and yawn,
As sleepy as can be.
You, too, will yawn if you will watch
To catch the yawn from me.
Yawn
     Yawn
         Yawn.

Hold up a picture of a child yawning and point to the picture when
you want the children to yawn.

LIP EXERCISE

I make my lips a round, round "oo"
When I say "too" and "do."
But they are wide apart, you see,
When I say "me" and "be."
And now I open wide my jaw
When I say "caw" and "saw."
So I will practice every day:
     "aw-oo-ee-aw,
     aw-oo-ee-aw."

Lip exercise is included in this chapter because best results can be obtained while the children are relaxed without tension in throat or face muscles. The "aw" sound used here may be related to the wide open jaw position in the poem "Yawning."

CAN'T YOU GUESS?

Teacher: Boys and girls, what are you doing?
Children: Can't you guess?
Teacher: Do you have your legs crossed?
Children: Yes, yes, yes.
Teacher: Boys and girls, what are you doing?
Children: Can't you guess?
Teacher: Are your hands held in your laps?
Children: Yes, yes, yes.
Teacher: Boys and girls, what are you doing?
Children: Can't you guess?
Teacher: Do you have your eyes shut with no peeking?
Children: Yes, yes, yes.
Teacher: Boys and girls, what are you doing?
Children: Can't you guess?
Teacher: Are you resting? Are you resting?
Children: Yes, yes, yes.

Let the voices get softer until they are just a whisper at the end. Emphasize clear enunciation, for example: *can't you* instead of *can chew*. This is a drill for the consonant "y" as well as a medium for readiness.

Listening and Sleepy Pictures

Cut from magazines pictures of animals and people who appear to be listening. Mount separately. Select pictures as needed and ask the children why the person or animal has to be a good listener. Select pictures of animals or persons sleeping and center the discussion around the way they sleep.

SLEEPY ANIMALS

When animals go to rest,
They sleep a funny way.
Bears sleep through the winter
When children like to play.
Robins stand upon one leg
With head tucked under wing.
Kittens curl up in a ball
With tail all in a ring.

All: So shut your eyes
And make a wish.
Sleep will come.
Hush, hush, hush.

Horses just stand very still,
And close their sleepy eyes.
Cows kneel down both front and back
Beneath the nighttime skies.
But boys and girls like you and me
All climb into their beds,
And on their fluffy pillows
They rest their sleepy heads.

All: So shut your eyes
And make a wish.
Sleep will come.
Hush, hush, hush.

BABY CHICK

Can you be a baby chick,
All downy, soft, and warm
Underneath your mother's feathers
Away out on the farm?
Sh . . . sh . . . sh . . . sh . . .
I will, I will, I will
Keep my body quiet,
And my eyelids still.

Teacher: Let us close our eyes and pretend to be fast asleep. When you are really asleep, your eyelids are still. They do not flutter at all. Now, I am going to read the poem again and I shall look all around the room to see how many children can keep their eyelids quiet.

RELAXATION DEVICE

My feet are still.
My legs are still.
My hands are folded and still.
My arms are still.
My shoulders are still.
My head is still.
My lips are still.
My eyes are still.
This is my quiet time.

Sit in front of the room as the children are taking their seats. Say the exercise in a low soft voice. Speak slowly. Talk to children singly when they do not seem to be able to control themselves. Impress upon them the importance of good self control. As you exemplify calm yourself, the children will catch the mood.

RELAXING TIME

I am sleepy ... very sleepy.
I want to stretch and yawn.
(Children stretch and yawn.)
I'll close my eyes and just pretend
That daylight time has gone.
(Children close eyes.)
I'll breathe so softly, be so still,
A little mouse might creep
Across the floor because he thought
That I was fast asleep.

    I'll listen for a bell to ring,
    (Pause while children listen.)
    Or maybe for a bird to sing.
    (Pause)
    I'll listen for a far-off noise
    That tells of busy girls and boys.
    (Pause)
    And then I'll be so very still;
    I'll drop my head far down;
    I'll cross my legs and make believe
    That I'm a sleepy clown.

Ask the children to tell what they heard while they were listening.

Wiggle Game

My lips can make a word,
And no sound will be heard.
Let's play the game today
To guess what I shall say.

First, watch my lips as I say the word *wiggle*. My lips are round when I say the "w" sound. When I make the "l" sound, you can see my tongue go up to touch the little shelf behind my upper teeth. Try it to see if your tongue and lips can do the same thing when you make these sounds. I am not going to use my voice at all. I shall ask you to wiggle only one part of your body at a time. Try to keep the other parts of your body still as we play the game.

> *(Lip formation)*   Wiggle your fingers.
> Wiggle your mouth.
> Wiggle your shoulders.

After we have wiggled all the parts of our bodies one at a time, there are no more wiggles left and we are quiet.

This is an exercise to increase attention span. It creates the listening habit. A child who has a hearing loss will benefit from such exercises as he will acquire the watching habit.

Let the children be the participants and you will soon learn which children are using their lips in speaking. If their lips cannot be "read" by others in the class, they will be made more conscious of their need for improvement.

The Still Game

Use a card with the word "Still" printed on it. Children are told that this card will be hidden somewhere in the room when they come in from recess or games. As soon as they see the card, they are to drop their heads on their desks or on their arms. After each child has discovered the card, the teacher says, "I am thinking of something that is still" (i. e., snow falling, or a flower growing). The children then are asked to think of something that is still. They take turns in telling their still thoughts.

CRICKET

Crickety cricket,
Crickety cricket,
Little, black, shiny
Crickety cricket;
Down in the thicket,
Down in the thicket,
Under the leaves in the brush
In the thicket;
Crickety cricket,
Crickety cricket,
Jump and sit straight,
Little, black, shiny cricket.

Children: Cricket, cricket, cricket
Rubs his wings.
"Cricket, cricket, cricket"
Is the song he sings.

This is a readiness jingle. Have the children say the word *cricket* softly in the last four lines. Rubbing palms of hands together creates a rhythmic effect imitative of a cricket.

The Magic Piano

The children are to chorus the replies which the animals, bird, and fish make to Goldie. If the teacher will repeat the refrain once or twice, the children will pick up the words and will eagerly join in the chorus each time a reply to Goldie is made. A music box, a piano, or a recording is needed in the telling of this story.

Goldie was a little girl who loved music. Whenever she heard a tune, she would stop her play and listen. She liked all of the instruments that made music, but best of all she liked a piano. Goldie wished more than anything in the world that she could play tunes on a piano.

One day Goldie had a birthday and Daddy brought home a little piano as a present for her.

"This is wonderful," cried Goldie, "but I cannot play."

"Never mind, Goldie," said Daddy, "one day you will be big enough to take music lessons. In the meantime, you will just have to make believe you are playing."

Goldie kept thinking and thinking about the music the little piano might play. She thought about it so much that she could almost hear the music.

In fact, one night as she was snuggled down in her warm little bed, she did hear music. It sounded exactly as if it were coming from her little piano. She listened very quietly. Surely enough. It was! *(Teacher plays a tune. At the end of the tune, the story continues.)* Goldie turned on the light beside her bed, but no one was there. She asked the cat, "Were you playing my piano?"

The cat replied, "Meow, meow, not I, not I;
　　　　　　To play a piano I'd never try."

The next night after Goldie had snuggled down under the soft warm blankets and turned off the light, she heard the music again. *(Music plays.)* When she turned on the light to see, no one was there at all. It was most strange, indeed. Goldie asked the dog, "Were you playing my piano?"

The dog said, "Bow-wow, bow-wow, not I, not I;
　　　　　To play a piano I'd never try."

The third night it was the same thing. As soon as the light went out, the music began to play. *(Music plays.)* Click, the light went on, but the mysterious piano player had disappeared.

Goldie asked the canary, "Were you playing my piano?"

The canary chirped, "Tweet, tweet, tweet, tweet,
　　　　　Not I, not I;
　　　　　To play a piano I'd never try."

As you might have guessed, the same thing happened the fourth night. *(Music plays.)* Click! Light on! Musician gone. Goldie asked the goldfish, "Were you playing my piano?"

The goldfish opened his mouth and said,
　　　"Gub, gub, gub, gub, not I, not I;
　　　To play a piano I'd never try."

Goldie thought and thought. Finally she decided that the light must be frightening the piano player away.

"I'll wait for the moon to come out," she whispered to herself; "then I'll be able to see who is playing my piano."

Goldie turned out the light and snuggled down under the soft blankets again. Soon the moon came out and its beams began to creep through the windows of the room. Slowly the bright rays stretched across the room until they reached the piano. And all at once . . . scamper, scamper, scamper. A tiny mouse ran out of its hole and went straight to the piano. And what do you know! He jumped up on the keys and ran up and down, up and down. *(Music plays.)* Goldie listened and enjoyed the tinkly tune. It was such fun, at last, to know who had been playing her piano. You can imagine what a good time the little mouse was having. Goldie listened for a long, long time and finally she drifted off to sleep as the little mouse kept right on playing.

Once this story has been used as a relaxation device by the teacher, she may use the music box, or record, again and again for the same purpose. The children will make the association with this story, or the teacher can retell a portion of it as the children rest after recess, games, or lunchtime.

Charlie Scarecrow

Children chorus the jingle of Inky Crow in order to have drill on the "k" sound in *crow* and *scarecrow*. For use in relaxation, the teacher should follow the instructions at the end of the story.

Charlie Scarecrow stood in the cornfield belonging to Farmer Jones. Charlie was there, of course, to scare crows away. This is, as you well know, the duty of all scarecrows. Farmer Jones had made Charlie because he was becoming alarmed at the way the corn was disappearing.

Charlie was a handsome fellow. He wore an old pair of Farmer Jones' trousers with patches on the knees, a red shirt that once belonged to Big Brother, and an old felt hat which had a hole in the top.

What a lazy looking scarecrow he was! His head drooped to one side. His arms hung limply and he bent over at the waist. In fact he seemed to be half asleep all the time. Farmer Jones had stuffed him with straw from the barn loft and the straw came out of his sleeves in long broom-like tufts.

Charlie's trouble started because he looked so lazy.

A very black, black crow named Inky used to sit on the branch of a tall tree that grew beside the cornfield. His tiny, glittering eyes would watch Charlie for a long time wondering just what he was going to do. When he did nothing, Inky would say in a hoarse voice,

"Caw, caw, caw. Haw, haw, haw.

I'm not afraid of that scarecrow."

Oh, he was a brave crow! He would fly to an ear of corn and peck all the kernels off before you could say "Jack Robinson." Then he would wink one eye and fly away saying:

"Caw, caw, caw. Haw, haw, haw.
I'm not afraid of that scarecrow."
Every day now, Inky sat in the tree and cawed:
"Caw, caw, caw. Haw, haw, haw.
I'm not afraid of that scarecrow."
And every day Charlie Scarecrow became unhappier because he could not chase Inky Crow out of the cornfield. Naturally, Farmer Jones grew angrier and angrier when more and more of the corn disappeared. Finally he said, "Charlie Scarecrow is not doing his duty. I simply cannot have all of my corn eaten by Inky Crow. I will make another scarecrow."

This time Farmer Jones made a great big scarecrow and named him Stuffy. Stuffy looked just like a soldier on guard. He was stuffed with so much straw that he was as stiff as a poker. His head was held high and he stood tall and straight. Not one inch did he move and my, how important he looked!

When Inky Crow saw two scarecrows in the cornfield, he did not know what to make of it. He sat in the tree for a long time and blinked his beady little eyes. Finally he grew hungry and decided to take a chance. So he flew down into the cornfield and found a nice ripe ear of corn. Peck, peck, peck went his bill and at the same time one eye was on Stuffy. Nothing happened. Neither scarecrow moved. Inky laughed:
"Caw, caw, caw. Haw, haw, haw.
I'm not afraid of that scarecrow."
All at once a brisk breeze came along. Charlie began to sway from side to side, back and forth, back and forth.

His arms flopped this way and that way and his head went around like a rubber ball. But Stuffy Scarecrow stood stiff. He never moved one fraction of an inch because he was stuffed with too much straw.

As Charlie Scarecrow flopped back and forth with the breeze, Inky began to get frightened. He had never seen Charlie act this way. With a loud "Caw," he flew out of that cornfield as fast as a jet plane and he never returned.

"Well, well," exclaimed Farmer Jones. "I think Charlie is the better scarecrow of the two after all. I shall leave him on guard in this cornfield from now on and take Stuffy away."

And Charlie stood in the cornfield with his arms limp, his head drooped to one side, and his body bent over at the waist, but he wasn't unhappy any longer. He knew that no crow ever again would say to him,

"Caw, caw, caw. Haw, haw, haw.
I'm not afraid of that scarecrow."

Teacher: Why was Charlie Scarecrow the better scarecrow? Can you show me how each scarecrow looked? Stand stiff like Stuffy . . . Now stand relaxed like Charlie . . . Pretend that the wind is blowing. It blows your body to the right and then to the left, back and forth, back and forth . . . Pretend that you are scaring crows away . . . Pretend that you are Inky Crow . . . Now let us make the scarecrow do several things:

> Scarecrow, scarecrow, turn around.
> Scarecrow, scarecrow, jump up and down.
> Scarecrow, scarecrow, arms up high.
> Scarecrow, scarecrow, wink one eye.
> Scarecrow, scarecrow, bend your knees.
> Scarecrow, scarecrow, flop in the breeze.
> Scarecrow, scarecrow, climb into bed.
> Scarecrow, scarecrow, rest your head.

The Tongue As a Speech Helper

Distinct articulation depends upon the control of and the flexibility of the tongue. The teacher can make a check on the tongue agility of her pupils very quickly by having them protrude their tongues and point them toward nose, chin, and cheeks. She will discover that many children make these movements slowly, with a lack of facility. It is these sluggish, retarded movements of many of the tongues which result in poor enunciation and indistinct speech.

Many children who cannot make the tongue-tip sounds, "t," "d," "n," and "l," are in trouble when it comes to correct placement. Imitation of the teacher is of great importance. She should make these sounds in an exaggerated manner so that the children can see her tongue touching the shelf (gum ridge) behind her upper teeth. A second step is for a child to use a mirror to watch his own tongue making these sounds in order to get the visual pattern as well as the feel of the sounds.

The tongue is again a problem when the child cannot make the "r" sound. He says "uh" for "r" and substitutes "w" for "r" in words, i. e., *wed wose* for *red rose.* The progress of re-education may be slow for the "r" sound because it is made inside the mouth and is difficult to imitate. See the section on the "r" sound for additional instructions for correction.

In the lateral lisp, which is a defective "s" sound, air slips over the sides of the tongue resulting in a cloudy type of "sh" sound. Tongue exercises can certainly be of help in gaining better control of the production of any sound in which the tongue is used.

Oral inactivity is not limited just to the tongue, but to the lips and the soft palate as well. A child who does not use his lips will frequently not use the tongue, and we may gather that he either feels inadequate about expressing himself or he does not feel up to par physically.

If a child is undernourished, the tongue, as well as other muscles of the body, may be flaccid. Proper nutrition should then be considered if there appears to be lack of muscle tone. The earlier such training and treatment are begun, the easier it will be to acquire new muscle patterns.

This training should be made as interesting as possible through the use of dramatization and play. The tongue can be identified as a real person taking an important role in oral language activities as the child views this new friend as his *own* speech helper. He takes pride in showing the class what his tongue can do, from tongue drills to the use of words with tongue sounds in them.

The stories and exercises given here are designed to make the tongue a more active participant in the speech of all children.

MR. TONGUE

In a little red house
Lives a little red man;
There's a gate in front of the house. *(Show teeth.)*
We open the gate,
And out he pops
As sly as a little gray mouse. *(Tongue between teeth)*
The little red man looks first to the right,
    (Tongue protruded to right)
And then to the left to see *(Tongue to left)*
If there's anyone coming to call on him.
Do you know what his name could be?
He looks to the north. *(Tongue up)*
He looks to the south. *(Tongue down)*
And then all around in a ring. *(Tongue circles.)*
Well, now that you know him,
You'll have such fun,
For he can do anything.

This tongue exercise should precede the drill on the voiceless "th" sound in order that the child may become aware of his tongue as a speech helper.

MY TONGUE

My tongue can do so many things.
Just look and you will see.

It can sweep, *(Tongue sweeps inside cheeks be-*
tween lips and teeth; lips are
closed.)

Go up and down, *(Tongue touches shelf behind*
upper teeth and sweeps down-
ward rapidly.)

And make the sound for T. *(Make voiceless*
sound "t" as in word
"too.")

Now it sweeps around, around. *(Repeat first movement.)*

Now way inside it sweeps. *(Sweep roof of mouth from*
front to back.)

Now it jumps gayly up and down. *(Tongue is protruded*
and moved toward
chin and then toward
nose several times
rapidly.)

Now out it slyly peeps. *(Tongue protrudes between*
slightly parted lips.)

My tongue can do so many things.

It's very useful, you can see.
It can sweep, *(Repeat above.)*
Go up and down,
And make the sound for T.

—FRANCES C. HUNTE

PINKY TONGUE

Teacher: Pinky Tongue lives in a little red house. The house is your mouth. Pinky Tongue has lots of work to do. He helps you to eat and he helps you to talk. He is a wonderful speech helper. He can peek out between your teeth and say "think" and you can see him rest on the little shelf behind your upper teeth when you say "little" or "lady." He can also say "t-t-t-t" and "d-d-d-d" very fast. Let us make our tongues do what Pinky Tongue does in this poem:

Pinky Tongue thought he would have some fun;
He crept out slowly to see the sun.
He looked up high, he looked down low,
To left, to right, then to and fro;
And then I heard him softly blow:
   "th," *(Voiceless)*
      "th,"
         "th."

The voiceless "th" sound should be used immediately in word recognition. Read a list of words, some of which contain the "th" sound in the initial position, and ask the children to raise their hands when they hear the sound that Pinky Tongue makes. See the word lists under the "th" section for suggestions. Since "f" is a common substitution for the voiceless "th" sound, words containing this sound should be included. The child may use a mirror to observe his tongue movements.

At the Circus

Susan was a little girl who liked to visit the circus. One day Mother said, "Susan, the circus has come to town. Let us go." So Susan put on her very best dress and bonnet and off they went. On the way they came to a brook. Over the brook was a bridge, and the bridge looked like this. *(Tongue tip is behind the lower teeth and the tongue itself is extended outward.)* They crossed the bridge and finally they arrived at the circus.

The first thing they saw was an elephant. Susan bought a sack of peanuts for him and, of course, the big elephant was delighted. His trunk went up and down as he reached for each peanut and put it into his large mouth. *(Tongue is extended toward the chin, then toward the nose. Repeat this movement several times.)*

Next were the monkeys who swung by their tails back and forth on the bars in their cages. *(Tongue extends out to the right of the mouth, then to the left.)* The monkeys said, "Ee-ee-ee," and seemed very friendly indeed.

The camels stood quietly chewing their cud, as camels do, and their jaws moved up and down like this. *(Tongue lies flat in the mouth as the jaw opens and closes.)*

Susan heard a low growly sound and there next door to the camels were three black bears. They growled, "Gr ... gr ... gr ..." They walked around and around in the pit in a circle. *(Tongue makes a circle inside the mouth.)* Then the bears turned around and walked the other way. *(Tongue reverses.)*

An organ grinder was playing a little tune that sounded like this: "La, la, la, la, la." *(Children sing "la" to a favorite song of their choice.)* A monkey crouched on the organ grinder's box and held out a cup for pennies. The cup looked like this. *(Tongue extended and raised at each side to form a cup.)*

Susan bought an ice cream cone and licked it like this. *(Tongue extended with a licking motion.)*

Soon Mother and Susan had seen almost everything at the circus and because it was late in the afternoon, they went home.

"Susan," said Mother, "you will have time for a nap before dinner."

Susan took off her best dress and put on her pajamas. She slipped into bed and was asleep in no time at all.

When she awakened, she was so rested that she remembered everything she had seen at the circus. Daddy was very much interested and he listened all during dinner to the adventures of Susan and Mother at the circus.

Little Brown Horse

Little Brown Horse lives in a barn, and the barn is your mouth. It is a red barn and it has a roof. You can feel the roof with your tongue, front and back. *(Children feel palates with tongue tip.)* You can also feel the floor and the sides. *(Tongue sweeps the roof, cheeks, and behind the lower teeth.)*

Little Brown Horse decided one day to take a walk. He walked straight out through the gate. He walked just as far as he could and then he stood still. *(Tongue protrudes and is held in a still position.)* Then he walked up the hill. *(Tongue protrudes toward nose.)* He ran down the hill. *(Tongue protrudes toward chin.)* Little Brown Horse was so thirsty that he took a drink from a trough that looked like this. *(Tongue protrudes and cups at the sides.)* He shook his head back and forth. *(Tongue protrudes and moves from left to right.)* Then he galloped down the road as fast as he could. *(Tongue makes clucking sound.)* Then he went back to his barn. He waved goodby to all of the animals *(Tongue makes lapping motion)* and then he shut the barn door for the night.

41

Exercises for the Tongue

1. Pretend that a train is coming. The wig-wag goes back and forth. It says: "Do not cross the track until the train goes by." Let us see if your tongue can be a wig-wag. Move it out to the right and then to the left, back and forth until the train is gone.

2. Make believe that your tongue is a telephone pole. Drop your jaw down and touch your tongue to the little shelf behind your upper front teeth. Hold it straight as can be while I count to five. Now hold it there and sing: "1........."

3. It is a very warm day. You need a fan. Fasten your tongue behind your lower teeth and extend it out and in, out and in several times.

4. Make the elephant say: "How do you do," with his trunk. It goes up toward your nose and down toward your chin.

5. Pretend that you are going down the slide in the school yard. Extend your tongue toward your chin very quickly.

6. Show us how kitty drinks her milk. Make your tongue go in and out, lap, lap, lap.

7. Show how your tongue would wave good-by to all of your friends. It goes up and down, up and down, just like a waving hand.

8. Pretend that your tongue is a mop. Make it clean the walls, the floor, and the roof of your mouth.

9. Make your tongue into a sidewalk and hold it as

still as you can. Extend your tongue straight out and hold it in a flat position.

10. Open your mouth and curl up the edges of your tongue to make a bowl. Look in the mirror to see if the sides of your tongue are up. Show your bowl to the class.

11. Pretend that your tongue is a merry-go-round. Let it circle around and around inside your mouth. Now make the merry-go-round circle the other way.

12. Be a clown and try to make your tongue touch your nose, your chin, your right ear, and your left ear.

PART II

SPECIAL HELP FOR SPECIAL SOUNDS

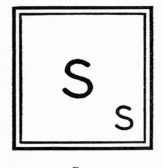

MAKING THE SOUND:

This sound is made with the lips in a slight smile position and the teeth nearly closed. The tongue is hidden behind the teeth. The tip of the tongue varies as to position. The vocal cords do not vibrate, and the soft palate is raised.

Observation has shown the "s" sound to be more frequently misarticulated than any other speech sound.

Call "s" the—

Teakettle sound

Snake sound

CORRECTING THE SOUND:

The most common defect here is a substitution of the "th" sound for the "s" sound, *thix* for *six, thithter* for *sister.* This is called the *central* or *protrusion lisp* because the tongue peeks out between the front teeth. The child must learn to keep his tongue behind his teeth. Encourage the child to use a mirror to help him acquire the proper position.

A second "s" deviation is the *lateral lisp* in which the air escapes laterally around the edges of a tongue held in a lazy flat position. It may be caused by the spacing or misalignment of the teeth or the shape of the jaw. The child must be taught proper tongue placement with exercises provided to increase tongue dexterity.

If the deviation is a *dominant* or *whistling s,* a sharp whistling noise accompanies the "s" sound. The child must be taught to make a softer "s" by using less force. Ear training is important here.

Other substitutions for the "s" sound may occur, such as "sh" or "t" or "d," but the techniques already mentioned will apply here.

Should the defect be due to teeth problems, medical or dental services should be advised.

The teacher will help the child produce the sound correctly by striving to bring into play as many of the child's senses as possible. A child, imitating a snake or a tea-kettle, and feeling the sound, hearing the sound, and watching the teacher make the sound correctly, will be more likely to use the correct sound as a regular pattern in his speech.

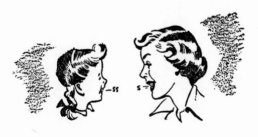

Typical Instructions:

The teacher might describe the sound "s" as follows: "Put your teeth together, very gently. Now smile and show the teeth. While your tongue is hiding, make the sound that a snake makes 's...s...s...' Listen to my snake: 's...s...s...' Does your snake sound like mine?"

Children may also be asked to imitate the sound of a teakettle giving off steam. The teacher should demonstrate first. Have the children feel the voice box while they are making the "s" sound and notice how quiet it is.

Words:

Initial	Medial	Final
snake	basket	miss
six	rooster	pass
spider	sister	kiss

In testing for a correct "s" sound, be sure to include words with the following blends, for a child may make the sounds correctly in some and not in others:

"sp"–speak	"st"–stop	"sk"–school	"sq"–square
wasp	first	skate	squeal
"sm"–smile	"sn"–snake	"sl"–sleep	"sw"–sweet
small	sneeze	slide	swing

46

grasps	baths	tents	box
laughs	lasts	tasks	horse

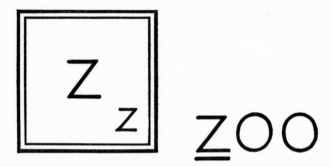

Z z ZOO

MAKING THE SOUND:

The "z" sound is made like the "s" sound, except that there is vocal cord vibration throughout. Have the children imitate the "bee" sound, "z...z...z...," and feel the voice box. They will be able to feel the vibrations and note the difference between the "snake" sound and the "bee" sound.

The "z" sound is one of the consonant sounds most frequently in error in the speech of both adults and children. See the section on correcting the "s" sound for techniques in helping to overcome "z" sound deficiencies.
Call "z" the—
    Bee sound

WORDS:

Initial	Medial	Final
zoo	fuzzy	bees
zebra	music	please
zero	daisy	nose

47

The teacher will note that in each of these words the final *s* is pronounced "z."

yours	sings	towns	hives	breathes
hills	rugs	tubs	thumbs	beds

GREEN SNAKE

A shiny green snake is sleeping.
When suddenly he awakes,
"s - s - s -"
Is the soft little sound he makes.

The shiny green snake is crawling
Over the leaves on the ground.
"s - s - s -"
Is his soft little hissing sound.

THE TIRE

I'll play that I'm a tire,
And take a breath just so;
Pretend that I am filled with air
From head down to my toe.
And then when I am very full,
I'll let it go like this:
Softly . . . softly . . . softly . . .
"s - s - s -"

Tell the children that a good "s" sound is made like steam coming from a teakettle. It hisses gently between the teeth. The best "s" sound comes from hearing acuity as the speech organs used in the production of this sound vary in shape with the individual. In this poem, have the children take a deep breath before the "s" is made so that the last line can be the prolongation of a single breath.

THIS IS THE GATE THE STEAM COMES THROUGH*

This is the gate the steam comes through.
"s - s - s -"
The steam can make a little song, too.
"s - s - s -"
John can make it and so can you.
"s - s - s -"
This is the place the sound must go.
"s - s - s -"
Hold back your tongue, don't let it show.
"s - s - s -"
Do it again, you soon will know.
"s - s - s -"
The steam can sing a gay little song.
"s - s - s -"
Push hard with your breath; now make it strong.
"s - s - s -"
Keep the gate shut; make the sound long.
"s----------"

—ANNA CARR

Teacher: Show me the gate the steam comes through. *(Children show closed teeth.)* Make the sound softly like the teakettle when it starts to boil. Now let the steam sound like a tiny whistle. Make a long "s------." Make it softer and softer until the steam is quiet.

**The Rehabilitation of Speech,* Revised Edition, 1947, by West, Kennedy and Carr. Harper and Brothers, publishers.

FIVE LITTLE PUMPKINS

Five children are chosen to be pumpkins, each child repeating his word when the time comes. The last child in line sits down after each repetition as the story progresses to "Four little pumpkins...," "Three little pumpkins...," etc. This continues until there are "No little pumpkins sitting on a fence waiting for Halloween."

Five little pumpkins sitting on a
    fence waiting for Halloween.
One said, "Say!"
One said, "See!"
One said, "Sigh!"
One said, "So!"
One said, "Soo-oo-oo!"

Have the fifth child draw out the "soo-oo-oo" to make it sound as spooky as possible in keeping with the spirit of Halloween.

MY FAMILY

Mother sits and knits so . . .
   This way, that way.
Mother sits and knits so . . .
   So . . . so . . . so.

Father drives the car so . . .
   This way, that way.
Father drives the car so . . .
   So . . . so . . . so.

Brother mows the lawn so . . .
   This way, that way.
Brother mows the lawn so . . .
   So . . . so . . . so.

Sister rocks her doll so . . .
   This way, that way.
Sister rocks her doll so . . .
   So . . . so . . . so.

Baby takes a nap so . . .
   This way, that way.
Baby takes a nap so . . .
   So . . . so . . . so.

Children may choose other occupations and pantomime them. Clapping may also be done for rhythmic effect.

SEE-SAW

See-saw, see-saw,
Up and down we go.
See-saw, see-saw,
High and then down low.
See-saw, see-saw,
Fun as you can see.
See-saw, see-saw,
Play the game with me.
See-saw, see-saw,
See-saw-see.

Let the children imitate a seesaw by extending their arms and rocking up and down in rhythm to the poem.

Exercise for Blends

"s - s - sm - sm" - smile, smile, smile.
"s - s - sw - sw" - sweep, sweep, sweep.
"s - s - sp - sp" - spin, spin, spin.
"s - s - sn - sn" - sniff, sniff, sniff.
"s - s - sk - sk" - skip, skip, skip.
"s - s - sl - sl" - slide, slide, slide.
"s - s - skw - skw" - squeak, squeak, squeak.
"s - s - st - st" -

Still . . .
Still . . .
Still . . .

Note that the *sq* blend in line 7 of the poem has been spelled as it is pronounced, "skw." Flash cards on which the words have been printed may be used. The children may also think of different words for each blend which can be dramatized. This exercise is for all "s" blends since a child will sometimes lisp on one blend and yet make the others correctly.

STOP FOR ME

Streetcar, streetcar,
Red as can be!
Streetcar, streetcar,
Stop for me!

Engine, engine,
Black as can be!
Engine, engine,
Stop for me!

Bicycle, bicycle,
Silver as can be!
Bicycle, bicycle,
Stop for me!

Pony, pony,
Brown as can be!
Pony, pony,
Stop for me!

The "st" blend is emphasized in this poem. Let the children choose different methods of transportation and select a color. Clapping will accentuate the rhythm.

NEW SHOES

I have a brand new pair of shoes,
Squeaky, squeaky, squeak.
Listen closely, they will speak,
Squeaky, squeaky, squeak.

"skw" or *sq* is one of the most difficult blends for children to make. Be sure that each child can make a *q*, which is a combination of "k" and "w," before attempting this blend.

EENCY WEENCY SPIDER

Eency weency spider
    Went up the water spout.
Down came the rain and
    Washed the spider out.
Out came the sun and
    Dried up all the rain,
And eency weency spider
    Went up the spout again.

               —TRADITIONAL

This jingle may be dramatized with hand action, crawling up the spout, rain dashing down, arms forming a round circle for the sun, and the spider crawling up the spout. Words that have the "s" sound are:

eency   weency   spider   spout   sun

JINGLE FOR MEDIAL "s"

Mister East peeked with one eye.
Mister West looked at the sky.
Mister North winked one, then two.
Mister South said, "How are you?"

JINGLE FOR FINAL "s"

Today I heard the iceman say,
    "Ice, ice, ice,
Who will buy my ice today?
    Ice, ice, ice."

SIX LITTLE MICE

All: Six little mice sat down to spin.
                  Pussy passed by and she looked in.
Low Voices: "What are you doing, my little men?"
High Voices: "Making coats for gentlemen."
Low Voices: "May I come in and bite off your threads?"
High Voices: "No, no, Miss Pussy, you'll bite off our
                      heads."
Low Voices: "Oh, no I won't. I will help you spin."
High Voices: "That may be true, but you can't come in."
                                          —MOTHER GOOSE

This jingle can be easily dramatized. Let half the class be cats and the other half mice. The repetition of the "s" sound will give drill for those children who need it.

Spoon Game

This game will aid in the correction of the "sp" blend. Obtain colored plastic spoons or paper spoons which may be painted different colors. Put them into a box and let the children take turns choosing a spoon. Each child holds up his spoon and says: "I chose a red spoon, green spoon," etc. The verbs may vary: I see, I bought, I have. Any particular sound may be worked on in this manner. Predominating sounds heard in the colors are "r" and "l":

"r"	"l"
orange	purple
brown	yellow
red	black
green	blue
purple	silver

Money Game

Have children make their own pennies for this game. Mount a series of pictures of objects that can be purchased at the grocery store.

Child: I would like to buy some peas.

Teacher: That will be seven cents, please.

Child: One, two, three, four, five, six, seven.

Teacher: Thank you.

Each article that a child buys should have a "s" or "z" ending, if possible, such as: *apples, carrots, cookies, etc.* Make each object cost six or seven cents to provide drill in the "s" sound and also to give experience in counting. Notice that these numbers contain the sounds of "th," "v," and "r" also. This game is excellent for speech survey purposes.

THE PARTY

Teacher: Some ice-cream cones went to a party. Each wore a dress of a different color. One was pink. That was strawberry. One was brown. That was chocolate. One was white. That was vanilla. One was purple. That was grape. One was yellow. That was lemon. One was green. That was lime. And one was orange, and that was orange.

Boys and girls, if you would like to hold one of the ice-cream cones that went to the party, you may ask, "May I have an ice-cream cone, please?" I will say, "What flavor would you like?" Then you may tell me the flavor. You may even tell me the color.

Ice-cream cones can be purchased from the grocery store or made from cardboard. Fill them with different colors of crepe paper to represent scoops of ice cream. For instructions on making a rack to hold the cones, refer to the section on "Devices to Use with This Book." This lesson is particularly valuable for drill on "s" in the medial position as in *ice cream.*

"I See" Game

Mount a series of pictures from magazines. Hold up one picture at a time for the class to see. Choose different children to tell the class what they see in each picture. Children should start each time by saying "I see..." Have a contest to discover who can name the most things containing the "s" sound.

The entire class may chorus the following sentence between pictures:

"See, see, what shall I see?"

SPLISH, SPLOSH, SPLATTER

Teacher: Raindrops falling all around,
  Making puddles on the ground.

All: Splish, splosh, splash;
  Splish, splosh, splatter.

Teacher: Five white ducks, with joyful quacks,
  Leave behind them muddy tracks.

All: Splish, splosh, splash;
  Splish, splosh, splatter.

Teacher: Across the barnyard, through the rain,
  Around the pond and back again.

All: Splish, splosh, splash;
  Splish, splosh, splatter.

Teacher: For it doesn't matter at all, you know,
  If a duck gets wet from head to toe.

All: Splish, splosh, splash;
  Splish, splosh, splatter.

Use this poem on a rainy day. Let the children imitate the ducks walking through the rain. This poem might be used as the preparation step for a discussion of how boys and girls should dress in rainy weather.

THIS IS THE HOUSE WHERE JACK LIVED

This is the house where Jack lived.

This is the stool that stood in the house where Jack lived.

This is Sam who sat on the stool that stood in the house where Jack lived.

This is the sauce that was made for Sam who sat on the stool that stood in the house where Jack lived.

This is the seed that was cooked in the sauce that was made for Sam who sat on the stool that stood in the house where Jack lived.

This is the thumb that pulled out the seed that was cooked in the sauce that was made for Sam who sat on the stool that stood in the house where Jack lived.

This is the mouth that kissed the thumb that pulled out the seed that was cooked in the sauce that was made for Sam who sat on the stool that stood in the house where Jack lived.

The magic flannel board may be used for this game which differentiates between the "s" and the "th" sounds. The objects in the story may be drawn or cut from magazines and mounted on flannel.

Objects: house, stool, Sam, sauce, seed, thumb, and mouth

"s" words: stool, house, stood, this, kissed, seed, sauce, Sam, sat

Voiceless "th" words: mouth, thumb

Voiced "th" words: this, that, the

Safety Game

Make a cardboard policeman with a round opening in each hand and in the cap. The openings are then covered with red, green, and yellow cellophane to represent traffic lights. As the child holds a flashlight behind each color, he says: "The policeman tells us to 'stop,' 'go,' 'wait.' "

Circus Wagon

Take a shoe box and cut strips around the sides for bars. Add four wheels and decorate to look like a circus wagon. Cut out pictures of circus animals and mount them on cardboard. The child chooses an animal and places it in the wagon saying: "A zebra (bear, lion, tiger) rides in my circus wagon."

"ks" Game

Cut socks of different colors from construction paper. Write or print a word having the "ks" blend on each sock. The child comes to the front of the room and says the following jingle as he draws a sock from the chocolate box:

> Once upon a time
> There was a little fox
> Who kept his socks
> In a chocolate box.
> He took out a (color) sock one day,
> And on the sock this word did say:

box	backs	wicks	fix	knocks
fox	tacks	tracks	sticks	books
looks	six	pecks	talks	decks

TIMMY TEAKETTLE

Tell children that they are to help Timmy Teakettle when it is time for him to speak aloud in the story. The teacher will soon find that, if children are encouraged to participate vocally in stories and poems, they will join in the telling whenever they can. The stories in this book take advantage of that fact by stressing correct production of a certain sound or sounds in each one.

Pictures will add to the effectiveness in the telling of any story.

Timmy Teakettle was very sad. He sat on the shelf with last year's Christmas toys and waited and waited for the little girl who owned him to play with him. But she never did. Timmy felt that he should be kept full of water, hot water, so that he could blow off steam and make a fine teakettle sound . . . "sssssss," like that.

The shelf where Timmy sat was very close to the kitchen, and often Timmy could hear water boiling. Sometimes it boiled loudly . . . "SSSSSSSSSS" . . . in a big pot, and sometimes it boiled softly . . . "sssssss" . . . in a little pot.

"How I wish that I could say 's,' " said Timmy Teakettle to himself. "I would make a lovely sound. It would sound just like a tiny whistle, very soft. It would be a pleasant sound that people would like to hear. I am sure that I could say 's' if someone would only fill me with water and put me on the flame to boil."

But no one paid any attention to Timmy Teakettle.

One day Timmy Teakettle decided to take matters into his own hands, or rather, into his own spout, for Timmy did not have any hands. He knew that he had to have water before he could make a fine teakettle sound, but he thought that he would try, anyhow.

He took a big breath and puffed out his teakettle cheeks, but all that came out was a "shshshshshshsh."

Timmy felt disappointed, but "I'll try again," he said.

He took a big breath and puffed out his teakettle cheeks, but all that came out was a "zhzhzhzhzhzhzh."

"Now, I know that is not the right sound," said Timmy. "That is the sound the vacuum cleaner makes."

So, Timmy took another big breath and puffed out his teakettle cheeks, but all that came out was "thththththth." *(voiceless)*

"Oh, no! that is the sound the old gray goose makes." And Timmy could have cried teakettle tears had there been any water inside him.

"I won't give up, though. I will try just once more." Timmy took a final great, big breath and puffed up his teakettle cheeks, but . . . but . . . but . . . all that came out was a loud "rrrrrrrrrrrrr" that sounded like Red Rooster when he woke Timmy up each morning. Poor Timmy. He felt that he just had to make steam, but what was he to do?

One day the little girl decided to have a tea party for her dolls. She set out her little table with chairs for the dolls and for herself. She placed a white cloth on the table and then set out her shiny toy dishes. She made sandwiches and salad . . . but something was missing. There was nothing to put into the cups.

The little girl thought and thought. Then she looked around the room. She glanced at the toy shelf and there . . . there was Timmy Teakettle, holding his breath for fear that the little girl would not see him.

But she saw him and exclaimed, "I shall have tea."

She ran to the shelf, got Timmy down and dusted him off. She filled the teakettle with water from the spout in the sink and set him on the stove. Timmy felt happy inside, because he knew that in just a few minutes he was going to be able to say something that he had been waiting a long time to say. The flame grew hot . . . and hotter . . . and Timmy began to go bubble-bubble-bubble-boil-boil . . . and he knew he was going to say something. So, he took a big teakettle breath and puffed out his teakettle cheeks and said . . . but, maybe you can guess what he said? That is right.

First he made a soft "sssss" . . . then a little louder "SSSSSSSSS" . . . and then a much louder "SSSSSSS."

Timmy Teakettle sat on the stove and sang and sang and sang and sang because he was so happy that at last he could make the teakettle sound.

Pretend that you are Timmy Teakettle and make a very soft "ssssssss." Take a big breath and make a long soft "sssssssss."

HONEY BEE

Where is little honey bee?
"zzzzzzzzz"
Buzzing in the honey tree;
"zzzzzzzzz"
Hear his drowsy sleepy tune
"zzzzzzzzz"
On a warm, bright afternoon.
"zzzzzzzzz"
Gathers pollen with his feet
"zzzzzzzzz"
From a clover blossom sweet.
"zzzzzzzzz"
Then he hurries to his home.
"zzzzzzzzz"
Honey's in the honey comb.
"zzzzzzzzz"
Tell me, little honey bee,
"zzzzzzzzz"
Are you making it for me?
"zzzzzzzzz"

The "z" sound in the refrain is continuous. The refrain may be varied by having the children use separate "z" sounds as: "z...z...z..."

ZIPPER PURSE

(Sing to the tune of "The Muffin Man.")

Mary has a zipper purse, a zipper purse,
    a zipper purse;
Mary has a zipper purse that goes,
    "zip, zip."

Bobby has a zipper purse, a zipper purse,
    a zipper purse;
Bobby has a zipper purse that goes,
    "zip, zip."

Place about a dozen small objects inside a zipper purse. As a child's name is mentioned in the song, he opens the purse on "zip, zip," and takes out one of the objects. He holds it up for the class to see and says, "I see a . . ." Of course, this game can continue until each child in the room has had a chance to open a zipper purse that goes "zip, zip." The teacher should observe each child carefully while he is having a turn in order to make certain that the "z" sound is being made correctly.

ZIP, ZIP, ZIP

Zip, zip, zip,
    Around the ice we go;
Zip, zip, zip,
    Dashing to and fro;
Zip, zip, zip,
    Zig-zags everywhere,
Zip, zip, zip,
    In the zero air.

If a recording of *The Skater's Waltz* is available, use it as background accompaniment in saying the poem. Let the children follow up the poem by pretending to be skating around the room in time to the music.

BUZZY

Buzzy is a little fly,
Very, very gay.
He begins his busy work
At the break of day.
Buzzy wakes me from my sleep,
    "z . . . z . . . z . . ."
Buzzy bites my toes,
    "zzzzz . . ."
Buzzy teases Grandmama
    "z . . . z . . . z . . ."
Buzzing on her nose.
    "zzzzzzzzzz . . ."

Ask the children to listen for words which have the "bee" sound in them. They may not get all of them until the poem has been repeated several times.

Buzzy   busy   toes   teases   nose   buzzing

FUZZY WUZZY

Class: Fuzzy Wuzzy is a funny, funny little bear:
No matter what we do to Fuzzy, Fuzzy doesn't care.
Tell us, Fuzzy Wuzzy, why you have a pointed
  nose;

Solo: "Because I need it, don't you see, I follow where it
  goes!"

Class: Tell us why your funny little eyes are small and
  round;

Solo: "Because the things I want to see are right here on
  the ground."

Class: Tell us why your ears are bigger than the rest
  of you;

Solo: "Because I like to hear the things I shouldn't
  listen to!"

Class: Tell us why you have no tail, you funny Teddy
  Bear;

Solo: "I guess the one who made me just forgot to put
  it there!"

Class: Oh, Fuzzy Wuzzy is a funny, funny little bear;
We like him 'cause no matter what we do he
  doesn't care!

—Conrad Wedberg

Additional drill may be obtained for the "s" and "z" sounds if the teacher adds the following words at the beginning of each solo line: "Said Fuzzy Wuzzy."

BUGS

There were twenty little bugs
That lived in twenty rugs.
They laid a hundred eggs,
And ran with eighty legs
To dark and foggy bogs
In search of twenty logs.
But twenty little frogs
Ate the twenty little bugs
That lived in twenty rugs,
And laid a hundred eggs,
And ran with eighty legs.

This is a nonsense drill for the "gz" blend.

ROSES

Teacher: What rose are you?
                 What color, your dress?
1st Child: I am a red rose.
2nd Child: I am a yellow rose.
3rd Child: I am a pink rose.
4th Child: I am a white rose.
All: We bloom to bring you happiness.

Children choose the roses they wish to represent. Explain to the children who can read that "s" sometimes sounds like "z." Examples: *has, was, rose, is,* and *does.*

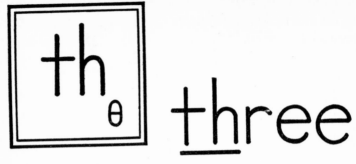

MAKING THE SOUND:

In making the voiceless "th" sound, as in *thank,* the lips are relaxed and slightly parted. The edge of the tongue is either pressed lightly against the biting edge of the upper front teeth or extended slightly between the upper and lower front teeth. The breath is forced gently out between the tongue and the teeth. The vocal cords do not vibrate. The soft palate is raised.

Voiceless "th" ranks high on the list of troublesome sounds, and among pre-school children is probably the most commonly misarticulated.

Call the voiceless "th" the—

Goose sound

CORRECTING THE SOUND:

If the substitution of the voiceless "th" is "f," show the child both sounds in similar words so that he may hear and see the difference, i. e., *three* and *free, thin* and *fin.*

The tongue may need to be protruded between the teeth more than usual at first, in order to get the feeling of the sound and to correct the substitution existing.

TYPICAL INSTRUCTIONS:

The teacher might describe the sound of the voiceless "th" as follows: "Smile and show your teeth just as you did to make the snake sound, 's-s-s.' This time, however, we do not hide our tongues. So let your tongue peek through your teeth. Now, blow gently. This is the sound the goose makes. Listen to my goose sound . . .'th-th-th' . . . make your goose sound like mine."

Have the children feel their voice boxes to note how quiet the sound is.

WORDS:

Initial	Medial	Final
thank	bathtub	mouth
thimble	birthday	tooth
three	toothbrush	bath

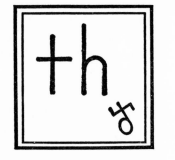 

MAKING THE SOUND:

The voiced "th" sound, as in *them,* is made like the voiceless "th," except that the vocal cords vibrate.

This sound is one of the most frequently defective consonant sounds. "d" is the usual substitution, i. e., *dis* and *fader* for *this* and *father.*

Have the children feel the vibrations in the voice box to distinguish this sound from the voiceless "th."

Call the voiced "th" the—

Fire engine sound

Airplane sound

WORDS:

Initial	Medial	Final
them	feather	smooth
their	mother	bathe
the	father	with

GRAY GOOSE

Gray goose, gray goose,
What do you say?
I say, " 'th . . . th . . .'
Many times a day;
'th . . .' at a rooster,
'th . . .' at a hen,
And 'th . . .' at any boy or girl
That comes near my pen."
Gray goose, gray goose,
Of what use are you?
"My feathers make fine pillows;
Would my lady like a few?"

Ask to see the tongue peeking between the teeth when the child makes the voiceless "th" sound. Say a group of words, some having the "goose" sound and some without the sound as *chair, three, floor, think.* See if the child can recognize the sound when he hears it.

THANK YOU

Thank you, Father.
Thank you, Mother.
Thank you, Sister.
Thank you, Brother.
If I am polite, you see,
Folks will be polite to me.

This jingle contains both the voiced "th" in the words *mother, father,* and *brother* and the voiceless "th" in the word *thank.*

70

THE SONG OF THE CRICKET

I heard a cricket sing this song:
   "Thumb, thumb, thumb."
He sang and sang the whole night long.
   "Thumb, thumb, thumb."
I tried to find him everywhere,
   "Thumb, thumb, thumb,"
In the closet, under a chair.
   "Thumb, thumb, thumb."
I waited till the break of day,
   "Thumb, thumb, thumb,"
But then that cricket hopped away.
   "Thumb, thumb, thumb,
    Thumb, thumb, thumb, *(softer)*
    Thumb, thumb, thumb." *(softer)*

Tell children that each time you hold up your thumb they are to repeat the word "thumb." This will give them a clue as to when it is their turn. Have the refrain fade away completely at the end of the poem as the cricket hops away. It is the voiceless "th" that is heard in the refrain.

I HEAR IT

I hear it in *thumb,* but not in *arm,*
I hear it in *thimble,* but not in *farm,*
I hear it in *bathtub,* but not in *door,*
I hear it in *three,* but not in *four,*
I hear it in *thread,* but not in *bat,*
I hear it in *toothbrush,* but not in *cat.*
    I open my teeth,
    Let my tongue peek through.
    I heard it again
    In *through* . . . did you?

Have pictures of the various voiceless "th" words in the poem, or better yet, have the object itself, such as thread, thimble, and toothbrush. Hold up the picture or the object as the word is called for in the poem. A different child may say each line with the entire class repeating the last four in unison.

This poem can be used as auditory training by asking the children to listen and then identify the sound being heard each time.

THANKSGIVING

We are thankful for home,
    We are thankful for food,
We are thankful for birds that fly.
    We are thankful for sleep,
  We are thankful for flowers,
    We are thankful for clouds in the sky.
We are thankful for picnics,
    We are thankful for rain,
And the rainbow that follows close by.

Children may have additional reasons for being thankful. Pictures containing objects for thankfulness can be held up by the teacher with children saying, "We are thankful," at the beginning of each sentence. The voiceless "th" is stressed.

"th" *Sound Game*

Have pictures of the various rooms in a house: living room, dining room, bath, and kitchen. The teacher tells the children that she is going to hide the THIMBLE in one of the rooms. One of the pictures is selected and children take turns guessing, "Did you hide the thimble in the bathroom?" "Did you hide the thimble in the kitchen?" until one guesses the room correctly. Let a child choose a picture and continue the game as before.

72

BIRTHDAY GIFTS

Children: Birthday, birthday; little boy has a birthday.
What will the cow give little boy
For a birthday present today?

Cow: Moo, moo, what shall I do
For a little boy who has just turned two?
I will eat some grass and give him a glass
Of milk; that is what I shall do.

Children: Birthday, birthday; little girl has a birthday.
What will the hen give little girl
For a birthday present today?

Hen: Cluck, cluck, what do I see?
A little girl who has just turned three.
I will sit on my nest and give her the best
Fresh egg for her birthday tea.

Children: Birthday, birthday; little boy has a birthday.
What will the dog give little boy
For a birthday present today?

Dog: Bow wow, bow wow, I just adore
A little boy who has just turned four.
We shall have such fun as we jump and run,
And play on the nursery floor.

Children: Birthday, birthday; little girl has a birthday.
What will the horse give little girl
For a birthday present today?

Horse: Neigh, neigh, now I arrive
To live with a little girl turned five.
She may feed me hay and ride all day,
Or harness me up for a drive.

73

THICKERY, THACKERY, THUMB

There was once a small boy who made so much noise
That his mother cried, "Oh," when he played with
his toys.

All: Thickery, thackery, thumb.
He tooted his horn and he thumped on his drum,
Till the neighbors all wished that his bedtime would
come.

All: Thickery, thackery, thumb.
He talked all the time and he would not sit still,
And he said, "I will not," instead of "I will."

All: Thickery, thackery, thumb.
Now, as you may have guessed, all his pets ran away,
And his playmates would call, but they never would
stay.

All: Thickery, thackery, thumb.
His toys were all broken, so what did he do?
He sat down and thought for an hour or two.

All: Thickery, thackery, thumb.
Then up the stairsteps and to bed he did creep.
Before you could count ten, he was quickly asleep.

All: Thickery, thackery, thumb.
Next day he was quiet, as still as a mouse.
Mother said, "Why, a different boy's in our house!"

All: Thickery, thackery, thumb.
And what really happened, I'll leave it to you,
When he sat down and thought for an hour or two.
Thickery, thackery, thumb.

This nonsense poem is used for drill on the voiceless "th" sound.
Questions may be asked by the teacher: What did the little boy think
about? Did people like him? Does sitting down and thinking help us?

THE LOST THIMBLE

This is a story for teaching the "th" sound. Objects containing the sound may be held up by the teacher. Repetition by Katy Kitten is effective. Example: "I have looked under the bath tub, the spool of thread, the bathroom scales, the three chairs, and the thimble is not there." This will give ample pupil participation to hold attention and to give repetitious drill on the sound wanted. At the end of the story, the teacher, who has had the thimble on her thumb all the time, may surprise the children by taking it from behind her ear.

Katy Kitten liked to sew. She made her own dresses. She even made her own hats. Always she carried a purse, and in that purse were *thread* and a *thimble*.

One day, just as she was ready to sew a few seams, she found that her *thimble* was gone.

"Oh, dear," sighed Katy Kitten, "I cannot sew without a *thimble*. What shall I do?"

She searched and searched and while she was searching, Old Mother Hubbard came along.

"Will you help me find my *thimble*?" asked Katy Kitten.

"Yes," answered Old Mother Hubbard, "if you will help me find my poor dog a bone."

Katy Kitten found the bone in a hurry and Mother Hubbard said, "Go home and look under the *bathtub*. Perhaps your *thimble* is there."

Katy Kitten went home and looked under the *bathtub*. No *thimble* was *there*. Since she was already in Mother Goose land, Katy Kitten decided to ask Bo Peep about the *thimble*. She said, "Bo Beep has lost her sheep many times and she has always found them. Perhaps she can help me to find my lost *thimble*."

Bo Peep was very sad because she had lost her sheep again.

"Please, Katy Kitten, will you help me find my sheep?" she asked.

"If you will help me find my *thimble*," replied Katy Kitten.

Of course the sheep were found in no time at all.

Bo Peep whispered, "Go home and look under *Father's* desk. Your *thimble* may be *there*."

Pitty-pat-pat, away went Katy Kitten to look under *Father's* desk. No *thimble*.

"Oh, oh, oh!" sobbed Katy Kitten.

"Why, what is the matter?" asked Jack Horner who was passing by.

"My *thimble* is lost. Please help me find it," pleaded Katy Kitten.

Jack Horner said, "If you will help me find a plum for my Christmas pie, maybe I can help you."

Katy Kitten ran to the orchard and brought a plum to put into the Christmas pie. Jack Horner pulled it out with his *thumb*. Then he said softly, "Look behind the red spool of *thread*."

Katy Kitten ran to the spool of *thread* and looked all around it, to the *north*, to the *south*, to the east, and to the west. No *thimble* was *there*.

Miss Muffet was sitting on a tuffet and she was very much excited.

"Please scare away *this* big spider," she cried.

"I will, if you will help me find my *thimble*," said Katy Kitten.

"Oh, yes," said Miss Muffet, "I will. Only please hurry!"

Katy Kitten made the spider run very fast and Miss Muffet whispered, "Just look under Baby's *thumb*."

Baby was sleeping soundly and Katy Kitten lifted her *thumb* carefully. But no *thimble*!

Well, *there* were a few more Mother Goose people to ask. One was Simple Simon.

When Katy Kitten told him about the lost *thimble,* he said, "Please give me a penny so that I can buy a pie."

Katy Kitten hurriedly found a penny for Simple Simon. He said, "Look under *Brother's* tricycle."

Alas! No *thimble*.

Along came Mary with the lamb trotting behind her.

"I *thought that* I heard you crying," said Mary. "How can I help you?"

"My *thimble* is lost," sobbed Katy Kitten.

"Never mind," comforted Mary. "I see *three* chairs. Look under each of them and perhaps you will find your *thimble*."

"*Thank* you," said Katy Kitten. One, two, *three*. No *thimble*.

Jack and Jill were coming up the hill.

"*This* pail is heavy," *they* said. "Will you help us carry it?"

"Gladly," said Katy Kitten.

All *three* of *them* carried the pail of water from the top to the bottom of the hill.

"Now, will you help me find my lost *thimble*?" asked Katy Kitten.

"Surely," said Jack and Jill. "Look under the *bathroom* scales."

Scurry, scurry went Katy Kitten. But no *thimble* was under the *bathroom* scales.

By this time Katy Kitten was becoming tired and sleepy. It was getting dark and she longed for her soft blanket.

"Ho, hum," yawned somebody, and looking around, Katy Kitten spied Willie Winkie. He was walking along the street carrying a lantern.

"Ho, hum," he yawned, "what are you doing here? You should be in bed asleep."

"My *thimble* is lost," said Katy Kitten in a wee, tired voice.

Willie Winkie yawned once more. Then he said slowly, "If I help you find your *thimble,* will you promise to go home and snuggle under your blanket until the sun comes up?"

"Yes, yes," said Katy Kitten anxiously.

"Then," said Willie Winkie, "look for your *thimble either* behind your right or your left ear."

Katy Kitten ran home and she looked behind her right ear and THERE IT WAS!

THUMPY, THE EASTER RABBIT

The children should be asked to repeat the jingle which Thumpy says each time he meets one of his friends. Colored paper eggs held up by the teacher will help the children to remember the sequence of colors. Specific drill on the voiceless "th" sound will be provided by having a thimble, a toothbrush, and a spool of thread. These objects can be held up by the teacher whenever they are called for in the story. After this is done several times, the children will join in wholeheartedly, chorusing the jingle and repeating the names of the three objects whenever necessary.

A series of pictures showing Thumpy talking to the hen, the owl, the duck, the birds, etc., will add visual attraction to the telling of the story.

Thumpy was a fuzzy little gray rabbit that lived in the forest. One day while he was hopping along, he heard a peep, peep. Then he heard a fluttering of wings. And looking behind him, he saw a tiny yellow bird.

"Hello, yellow bird," greeted Thumpy.

"Hello," said the yellow bird in a wee voice, "I have something important to tell you. Bend your ear and I will whisper it to you."

The yellow bird whispered something that made Thumpy run for home as fast as he could, hippety-hop. When Thumpy arrived at the rabbit hutch, he looked at his calendar. Surely enough! April had come. And of course April meant Easter.

"That little yellow bird was right," said Thumpy. "Easter is almost here and I do not have any Easter eggs ready for the boys and girls. That will never do. I had better get started right now."

Off Thumpy went to see his friend, the hen.

"Three eggs for Easter,
Please give them to me.
I need red ones, and green ones, and yellow
ones, too;
Orange ones, and purple ones, and some that
are blue."

"I can't give you three eggs for Easter," said the hen, "until you give me a thimble, some thread, and a toothbrush."

"Very well," replied Thumpy. And he ran home to get a thimble, some thread, and a toothbrush.

"Here are the things you asked for," stated Thumpy, upon his return, "a thimble, some thread, and a toothbrush."

"And here are three eggs for Easter, a red one, a green one, and a yellow one."

Now, Thumpy had three eggs for Easter, but when he thought of all the boys and girls in the world, he decided that three eggs would not do. However, if each of his friends gave him three eggs, perhaps then he would have enough. So away he went to see the owl.

"Three eggs for Easter,
Please give them to me.
I need red ones, and green ones, and yellow
ones, too;
Orange ones, and purple ones, and some that
are blue."

"I can't give you three eggs for Easter," said the owl, "until you give me a thimble, some thread, and a toothbrush."

"Very well," replied Thumpy. And he ran home to get a thimble, some thread, and a toothbrush.

"Here are the things you asked for," said Thumpy, when he returned, "a thimble, some thread, and a toothbrush."

"And here are three eggs for Easter, an orange one, a purple one, and a blue one."

Now Thumpy had six eggs for Easter. Then he went to see the duck.

"Three eggs for Easter,
Please give them to me.
I need red ones, and green ones, and yellow
ones, too;
Orange ones, and purple ones, and some that
are blue."

"I can't give you three eggs for Easter," said the duck, "until you give me a thimble, some thread, and a toothbrush."

"Very well," replied Thumpy. And he ran home to get a thimble, some thread, and a toothbrush.

"Here are the things you asked for," stated Thumpy, upon his return, "a thimble, some thread, and a toothbrush."

"And here are three eggs for Easter, a red one, a green one, and a yellow one."

Now, Thumpy had nine eggs for Easter, but that was still not enough. So, away he went to see his friends the birds.

"Three eggs for Easter,
　　Please give them to me.
　　I need red ones, and green ones, and yellow
　　　　ones, too;
　　Orange ones, and purple ones, and some that
　　　　are blue."

"We can't give you three eggs for Easter," said the
birds, "until you give us a thimble, some thread, and a
toothbrush."

"Very well," replied Thumpy. And he ran home to
get a thimble, some thread, and a toothbrush.

"Here are the things you asked for," stated Thumpy,
upon his return, "a thimble, some thread, and a toothbrush."

"And here are three eggs for Easter, an orange one, a
purple one, and a blue one."

Now, Thumpy had twelve eggs for Easter. That
would be enough for a beginning on Easter Eve. Home
Thumpy went with his eggs, hippety, hippety hop.

He waited until the night before Easter. Then he went
out and hid his eggs for the boys and girls. Finding good
hiding places took a long time, and Thumpy was a tired
little rabbit when he finally arrived at the rabbit hutch.
He climbed into his blue pajamas, lighted a candle, and
off he went to bed . . . but all at once he spied something
big and round sitting over in the corner. Was it a ball? . . .
No! Was it a balloon? . . . No! It was an egg, a round
Easter egg.

"How strange!" thought Thumpy. "A round Easter
egg. It looks very tasty. I am too tired to eat it tonight,

though. I will have it for breakfast on Easter morning."

The next morning Thumpy got up, washed his face and paws, and prepared to eat his beautiful round Easter egg. But when he went to get it, there was no Easter egg. All he could find were some pieces of the shell.

"I wonder who ate my egg?" Thumpy said in a sad voice.

Then, from somewhere behind him came three tiny voices, "No one ate it. No one at all. We were hiding inside of the Easter egg . . . to surprise you."

Thumpy turned around with a jump . . . and there in the garden wheelbarrow were one . . . two . . . three little Thumpys.

"We've come to live with you," they said with a merry laugh. "Aren't you pleased?"

"Oh, yes," laughed big Thumpy right back. "Now I will have three little Thumpys to help me hide Easter eggs when next Easter time comes."

FIRE ENGINE

Show children that in making a good "fire engine" sound, the tongue peeks between the teeth just as it did when the "goose" sound was made. The "fire engine" sound has voice. Feel it in the words: *this, that, mother, father, brother,* and *feather.*

"th ... th ... th ... th ..." *(Voiced)*
Goes the fire engine.
"Get out of my way;
I race and I hurry,
And so I say,
'th ... th ... th ... th ...' "
    The fire engine red
    Comes out of his shed;
    " 'th ... th ... th ...'
    I see a big fire
    With flames growing higher.
    'th ... th ... th ...'
    Please go, firemen,
    As fast as you can.
    'th ... th ... th ...' "

AIRPLANE

The airplane also makes the voiced "th" sound. Pretend that you are an airplane. Let your tongue touch your teeth and say "th ... th ..."

I saw an airplane yesterday
As I was going out to play.
    "th ... th ... th ..."
It circled high, around, around,
And then it landed on the ground.
    "th ... th ... th ...
    th ...."

84

MAKING THE SOUND:

Generally speaking, the "r" sound may be made in this way: open the mouth and say "ah"; with the mouth in this position, let the tongue curl up and back toward the roof of the mouth. The "ah" should change to a semblance of "r" or even a pure "r." In normal speech, however, the tongue is elevated so that its sides contact the upper side teeth and the tip points upward. The soft palate is raised; the teeth and lips are slightly parted with the lips tending to be rounded; there is vocal cord vibration.

The "r" sound is often difficult for children because the ability to articulate this sound in words usually comes late in a child's speech development.

Call "r" the—

Rooster sound

Growling dog or lion sound

CORRECTING THE SOUND:

Throughout this section the initial and the medial "r" will be stressed, for the final "r" sound is not pronounced or stressed in some parts of the country. The classroom teacher should remember also that the medial "r" sound is slighted in certain Southern American and Eastern American speech. It is important that the teacher consider the regional speech patterns of the area in which she teaches when giving instruction on the "r" sound.

Since the "r" is corrected primarily through hearing, it is important that the child hear himself make the sound correctly. The device of saying "ah" and letting the tongue curl up and back will enable almost any child to produce an "r" sound. Once the child hears himself make the sound, the exaggerated mouth position of "ah" can be reduced. Feeling the position of the tongue on "ee" and then working toward "r" will sometimes produce results. Activity through "r" blends, such as *pr, dr, gr,* and *tr* may help.

The "w" sound is the most frequent substitution for "r," and differentiation of words, such as *wide* and *ride,* and *weed* and *read,* will give ear training.

It is difficult to tell children where to place the tongue to get results; where one method will work, another will fail. Thus it is more satisfactory to experiment with various placements in working from the known to the unknown and to depend largely upon the ear.

TYPICAL INSTRUCTIONS:

The teacher might explain the "r" sound as follows: "Watch my tongue while I make the sound of 'ah.' It is flat in my mouth. Let's all say 'ah' and feel how flat our tongues are. Watch my tongue this time . . . I am going to make it curl up toward the top of my mouth . . . Listen closely, because I will make a new sound as my tongue moves up . . . 'ah-er.' . . . Did you see my tongue change positions? . . . Did you hear the new sound? . . . Now let

us all make our tongues curl up to say the new sound . . .
'ah-er.' . . . We call this sound the 'rooster' sound. . . .
Listen and you will hear why it is called the 'rooster' sound
. . . 'r-r-r-r-r.' . . . Let us make our tongues roll up this time
and say the 'rooster' sound . . . 'r-r-r-r-r.' . . . Did your
rooster sound like mine?"

(Caution: the teacher should warn against letting the
tongue curl too far back in the mouth. If it does, the "r"
sound may assume too guttural a quality.)

WORDS:

Initial	Medial	Final
rabbit	carrot	father
red	hurry	car
rose	purple	chair

BLENDS:

"pr"–pretty   "kr"–crow
    prayer   cricket
"br"–brother   "gr"–grape
    broom   green
"tr"–train   "dr"–dress   "fr"–frog   "rk"–fork
  trunk   drink   fruit   cork

ROOSTER

Every day the rooster crows,
    "r, r, r, r, r,"
As he stretches on his toes,
    "r, r, r, r, r."
He flaps his wings and shakes his head.
    "r, r, r, r, r,"
And says, "Get up, you sleepy head,
    'r, r, r, r, r.' "

It is common for a child to say *wed* for *red*. "r" is one of the last consonant sounds which a child learns to make. The "r" sound may have looked like "w" on the lips when he was imitating speech. The child may not have heard the sound correctly. The substitution of the "r" may be "uh" until he has had sufficient ear training.

BLACK BEAR

The old black bear lives in a zoo.
He walks around, around.
He growls and growls as all bears do,
And makes this growly sound:
"r . . . r . . . r . . . r . . . r . . ."

RAG MAN

In the following jingle, "r" precedes the vowel sound of a short *a*. Having the child work from the vowel to the "r" will sometimes help him to acquire the sound

The raggedy man on the corner cries,
"Rags, rags, rags,
New rags, old rags, any size,
Rags, rags, rags.
Have you any rags today?
Rags, rags, rags.
For each a penny I will pay.
Rags, rags, rags."

LION

The lion in the circus roars.
He crouches down upon all fours.
"Grrrrr . . . grrrrr . . . grrrrr . . ."
I think I'd make a noise that way,
If I were in a cage all day.
"Grrrrr . . . grrrrr . . . grrrrr . . ."
Show how the "r" sound is prolonged when the lion growls.

RAINDROPS

Solo: When it is raining, I like to be
Out where the raindrops can splash on me.

Children: Raindrops, raindrops,
Splash, splash, splash;
Raindrops, raindrops,
Splash, splash, splash.

Solo: I put on my rubbers and button my coat,
Then find a small river to sail my boat.

Children: Raindrops, raindrops,
Splash, splash, splash;
Raindrops, raindrops,
Splash, splash, splash.

The refrain said by the children includes the initial "r," the "dr" and "sp" blends, and the "sh" sound.

TELEPHONE

1st group: "Ring, ring, ring, ring,"
I can hear the telephone say,

2nd group: "Ring, ring, ring, ring,
Is anyone at home today?

3rd group: "Ring, ring, ring, ring,
Answer quickly! Stop your play!

All: Ring, ring, ring!"

RAPPETY RAP

Rappety rap, rappety rap,
Why are you making a noise like that?
Rappety rap, rappety rap,
When Daddy is trying to take a nap?

SEE THE WINDMILL TURNING

See the windmill
    now is turning,
        turning, turning,
            round and round.
Round and round
    its arms are turning,
        round and round
            with grinding sound.
                —*Old French song*

Have the children revolve one arm to imitate the turning of the windmill. Watch the lips of the children as they make the initial "r" with the diphthong "ou" as in *round*. The lips should move from a closely rounded position for "r" to an expanded and then closely rounded position as the diphthong "ou" is formed.

MOUSIE BROWN

Little mousie brown,
    He ran up the candlestick
        To eat some yellow tallow,
            And he could not get down.
He cried, "Ma-ma, ma-ma, ma-ma,"
    But mama was in town;
        And so he rolled up in a ball,
            And rolley, rolley, rolley, rolled,
            And rolley, rolley, rolley, rolled,
                And rolled
                    himself
                        right
                            down.
                —*Adapted from a Chinese nursery rhyme*

Fingers pantomime climbing up the candlestick and rolling down. Prolong the "r" slightly before going into the vowel sound of long *o*.

90

MERRY-GO-ROUND

Around and around on the merry-go-round,
When I visit in circus town.
A nickel to pay for the music to play,
As the horses go up and down.

Around and around on the merry-go-round;
I may choose any horse to ride,
With a shiny, bright harness and flowing mane,
And a saddle to sit astride.

Around and around on the merry-go-round
On a horse to pretend for a while,
As I sit so grand with the reins in my hand
In my very best circus style.

THE RAIN

Quietly, so quietly, drift in from the sea,
Dark clouds, gray clouds, heavy as can be.
    Rain, rain, rain,
    Drip, drip, drop.
Over city, over hill, over farm and plain,
Over highway straight and smooth, over moving train.
    Rain, rain, rain,
    Drip, drip, drop.
The happy day grows very dim, the sunshine disappears,
When suddenly the sky above begins to shed its tears.
    Rain, rain, rain,
    Drip, drip, drop.
The rain is fresh, the air is sweet, the patter all around
Makes noises on the roof tops and drips slowly to the
  ground.
    Rain, rain, rain,
    Drip, drip, drop.
And as we listen to the rain, it makes us wonder why
The heavens hide behind dark clouds and then begin
  to cry.
    Rain, rain, rain,
    Drip, drip, drop.

The "dr" blend is used in this poem. Children say the refrain each
time, using hands to imitate rain falling.

RIDDLE-RIDDLE-REE

Children: Riddle-riddle-ree,
What color do I see?

Teacher: It starts with the "rooster" sound,
And ends with a D. *(red)*

Children: Riddle-riddle-ree,
What color do I see?

Teacher: In the middle is the "rooster" sound.
It starts with a P. *(purple)*

Children: Riddle-riddle-ree,
What color do I see?

Teacher: The "rooster" sound is second,
And it starts with a G. *(green)*

Children: Riddle-riddle-ree,
What color do I see?

Teacher: The "rooster" sound is second,
And it starts with a B. *(brown)*

Children: Riddle-riddle-ree,
What number do I see?

Teacher: In the middle is the "rooster" sound.
It ends with double E. *(three)*

Children: Riddle-riddle-ree,
What number do I see?

Teacher: It ends with the "rooster" sound,
And follows number three. *(four)*

This can be used as a reading readiness game by having the colors
and numbers written out on cards. Children guess the color or number
from the clues given in the poem. The capital letters are pronounced as
letters of the alphabet.

HURRY, HURRY

Hurry, hurry, hurry, hurry,
Fire engine races by.
Hurry, hurry, hurry, hurry,
Airplane zooming through the sky.

Hurry, hurry, hurry, hurry,
Streamline train goes out of sight.
Hurry, hurry, hurry, hurry,
Streetcar moving through the night.

In a hurry, people skurry;
In a hurry, snowflakes flurry.
People, snowflakes, streamline train,
Fire engine, streetcar, plane—
One and all are in a hurry;
Everything and everybody
Hurry!
　　Hurry!
　　　　Hurry!

The medial "r" is stressed in the word *hurry*. The word may be used
on a flash card and held up each time the children are to say *hurry* in
the poem. Try to obtain pictures of the various modes of transportation
mentioned.

"r" Combination Drill

Find pictures to illustrate the blends: "tr," "pr," "br," "kr," "dr," "fr," and "gr."

Tray, try, tree; trains I can see.
Pray, pry, pree; presents I can see.
Bray, bry, bree; bridges I can see.
Kray, kry, kree; crickets I can see.
Dray, dry, dree; drums I can see.
Gray, gry, gree; grapes I can see.

Recognition of Final "r"

I know a quiet family; their name is very queer;
But how they like to listen, and oh, how they can hear.

cheer	fear	hear
ear	steer	near
clear	dear	peer
shear	tear	jeer

A large picture of an ear is drawn on the blackboard and filled with the above words. This is an example of a word family used in teaching phonics.

FRISKY PONY

Children will imitate the "rooster," "dog," and "goose" sounds and say repetitive phrases with the teacher as the story progresses. A prolongation of initial "r" in the first *run* will give children the cue in starting the rhythmic jingle. See that lips do not protrude forward when saying the word *run*.

Frisky Pony was a little black pony with a beautiful brown and white mane and tail. He liked to run, and that was why he was called Frisky Pony. But Frisky Pony had no master, so he was unhappy. He looked everywhere for a master named Robert, but whenever he saw a little boy that looked as if he might want a pony, the boy's name was never Robert. It was Sam or Dick or Charles or Jimmy. Why, it was no fun at all to run about with no master to guide the reins.

One day as Frisky Pony was galloping along waving his tail in the wind, he met a dog. The dog said, "Gr . . . gr . . . gr . . . Why are you running, Frisky Pony?"

"I am running to find a master named Robert," said Frisky Pony.

"Well," said the dog,

"Run, run, run, run, run, run, run, run,
Run, little pony, run."

Soon Frisky Pony met a goose. "th . . . th . . . th . . . ," said the goose. "Why are you running, Frisky Pony?"

"I am running to find a master named Robert," said Frisky Pony.

"Well," said the goose,

"Run, run, run, run, run, run, run, run,
Run, little pony, run."

Next, Frisky Pony met a rooster.

"r-r-r-r-r," crowed the rooster. "Why are you running, Frisky Pony?"

"I am running to find a master named Robert," said Frisky Pony.

"Well," said the rooster,

"Run, run, run, run, run, run, run, run,
Run, little pony, run."

After a while Frisky Pony came to a tree. He decided to stop a while to rest, but whom should he see far, far

away in the distance but a little boy running toward him.
As the little boy came closer, Frisky Pony saw that he had
a halter in his hand. The little boy came very close to
Frisky Pony.

"Are you looking for a master, Frisky Pony?" asked
the little boy.

"Yes, indeed," answered Frisky Pony. "Is your name
Robert?"

"Why, how did you know?" asked the little boy, very
much surprised. "Of course my name is Robert. Please
let me get onto your back and take a ride."

Frisky Pony was very happy as Robert mounted him
and took the reins in his hand.

"Shall we run?" asked Frisky Pony.

"No," replied Robert, "running is too exciting. Let
us trot. So . . . trot, trot, trot, trot, trot, trot, trot,

      Trot, Frisky Pony, trot."

Repeat the final refrain until the words are fainter and fainter to
indicate Frisky Pony and Robert riding away in the distance.

TOMMY TURKEY

Have the children say the repeated refrains. The medial "r" sound in *turkey* can be emphasized or elongated. The magic flannel board is used for the different colored turkeys and the characters that are encountered. Vowels are emphasized in "ha, ha, ha; he, he, he."

Tommy Turkey was a beautiful gobbler. His wattles were bright red and his feathers were many colored. When he strutted, they swept along the ground and made a rustling sound like dry leaves at autumn time.

Tommy Turkey, one bright November morning, decided to strut down the road. It was nearing Thanksgiving time, but since no one had said a word to him about it, he was happy and unafraid. As he was strutting along he spied a blue bird. The blue bird saw him and sang:

"Ha, ha, ha; he, he, he;
 You're the funniest turkey
 I ever did see."

Tommy Turkey said:

"Oh, dear, oh, dear; oh, me, oh, me;
 Why am I the funniest turkey
 You ever did see?"

The blue bird answered: "Because you should be blue like me. That is the only bright color for anything to be. Everything in the world should be blue."

So Tommy Turkey went home and dyed himself blue. He continued on his walk and all at once he met a rabbit who laughed:

"Ha, ha, ha; he, he, he;
    You're the funniest blue turkey
    I ever did see."
Tommy Turkey said sadly:
    "Oh, dear, oh, dear; oh, me, oh, me;
    Why am I the funniest blue turkey
    You ever did see?"
"Because," said the rabbit, "you should be white like me. Why do you not go home and do something about it?"

So Tommy Turkey went home and dyed himself white like the rabbit. And just as he started out to walk again, he met a little green garter snake who laughed:
    "Ha, ha, ha; he, he, he;
    You're the funniest white turkey
    I ever did see."
"I have dyed myself blue and I have dyed myself white," said Tommy Turkey. Then he said:
    "Oh, dear, oh, dear; oh, me, oh, me;
    Why am I the funniest white turkey
    You ever did see?"
"Well," replied the snake, "green is such a nice cool color. The grass is green. In fact many important things are green. You should be green, too."

Tommy Turkey straightway went home and dyed himself green.

Next he saw a red-headed woodpecker pecking on the oak tree. When the woodpecker saw Tommy Turkey, he stopped pecking. He opened his bill and laughed:
    "Ha, ha, ha; he, he, he;
    You're the funniest green turkey
    I ever did see."

By this time Tommy Turkey was getting very much discouraged. He sighed:

"Oh, dear, oh, dear; oh, me, oh, me;
Why am I the funniest green turkey
You ever did see?"

The red-headed woodpecker said, "Whoever heard of a green turkey? Have you noticed what a lovely red head I have? Red is such a brilliant color. Why do you not dye yourself red?"

So Tommy Turkey went home and dyed himself red like the woodpecker's head.

Soon he heard another laugh and looking around, he saw a little yellow chicken who peeped:

"Ha, ha, ha; he, he, he;
You're the funniest red turkey
I ever did see."

Tommy Turkey cried:

"Oh, dear, oh, dear; oh, me, oh, me;
Why am I the funniest red turkey
You ever did see?"

The chicken answered, "Whoever heard of a red turkey? Why are you not a cheerful yellow color like me?"

As you might guess, Tommy Turkey went home and dyed himself yellow. He thought that surely he had done the right thing this time, but as he was walking along, he met a pussy cat. The pussy cat sniffed:

"Ha, ha, ha; he, he, he;
    You're the funniest yellow turkey
    I ever did see."
Tommy Turkey wept:
    "Oh, dear, oh, dear; oh, me, oh, me;
    Why am I the funniest yellow turkey
    You ever did see?"
The pussy cat whispered, "I will tell you a secret. If you will dye yourself purple like a flower, everyone will like you."

Well, of course, Tommy Turkey did as the pussy cat told him and dyed himself purple like a flower.

"Quack," said a duck that was waddling along. "What is this?

    "Ha, ha, ha; he, he, he;
    You're the funniest purple turkey
    I ever did see."
Tommy Turkey was feeling quite sad by now. He looked anxiously at the duck and asked:
    "Oh, dear, oh, dear; oh, me, oh, me;
    Why am I the funniest purple turkey
    You ever did see?"
The duck quacked, "I do not like purple as a color. Orange is much more gorgeous. My bill is orange, and I think that is the best color in the whole wide world."

In a few minutes, Tommy Turkey was orange just like the duck's bill. As he started to resume his walk, there appeared a man and a woman. They stopped and stared at him for a long time and finally they laughed:

"Ha, ha, ha; he, he, he;
    You're the funniest orange turkey
    We ever did see."

"Oh, dear," sobbed Tommy Turkey, "I have dyed myself blue, green, red, purple, yellow, white, and orange, and I have pleased no one. What am I to do?"

"Never mind," said the man and the woman. "Just come with us and we will fix everything. We will make you into a nice color that will please everybody . . . a nice Thanksgiving color."

So Tommy Turkey walked home with the man and the woman, and in a short time, there he was on a platter, a golden brown juicy turkey all ready for a Thanksgiving dinner.

Teacher: Why was Tommy Turkey a foolish turkey?
    If we try to please everybody, what usually
        happens?
    Did you expect this to happen to Tommy
        Turkey?
    Should he have stayed the way he was in the
        first place?

l leaf

MAKING THE SOUND:

Let the jaw drop down to the position of "ah." Raise the tip of the tongue to press lightly against the ridge behind the upper teeth. The vocal cords vibrate and the soft palate is raised. The width of the mouth opening will vary according to the vowel following the "l."

"l" is one of the consonant sounds frequently misarticulated in children's speech. The usual substitutions are "y" and "w," i. e., *yady* or *wady* for *lady*.

Call "l" the—

Singing sound

Telephone sound

CORRECTING THE SOUND:

The use of a mirror will be most helpful in showing a child the position of the tongue. As soon as he has the position, use the syllable *la* to let him feel the correct movement of his tongue. It is advisable to combine the initial "l" with vowels, as in *la, lee, loo,* before attempting the consonant blends: *kl, bl, fl, gl,* and *sl.* From syllables attack words as soon as possible in order to develop meaning for the child.

WORDS:

Initial	*Medial*	*Final*
lamp	yellow	bell
leaf	elephant	doll
letter	telephone	school

BLENDS:

"pl"–play	"gl"–glove	"lk"–silk
plow	glad	milk
"bl"–black	"fl"–flower	"lf"–elf
blue	flame	wolf
"sl"–sleep	"lm"–film	"ld"–held
slow	elm	rolled
"kl"–clean	"lp"–help	"rl"–curl
clay	scalp	girl

TELEPHONE WIRES

As I walked to school one day,
I heard the telephone wires say,
"l...l...l..."
It sounded like a little song.
I sang it, too, as I strolled along:
"l...l...l..."

The teacher asks to see the tongues of the children as they make the "l" sound. This will enable her to tell whether or not the children have the tips of their tongues touching the gum ridge behind their upper front teeth.

The "l" sound may be carried into the syllable *la* and used in place of words in a favorite tune like *London Bridge Is Falling Down*.

MY GATE

I have a white gate
That is pretty and clean,
For I brush it twice a day.
It opens ... and closes ...
And in between,
My tongue comes out to play.
    Loo, lee, lah,
    Loo, lee, lah.
    My tongue can do things, if it tries.
    Loo, lee, lah,
    Loo, lee, lah,
    It takes its morning exercise.

Discuss the tongue and show children that it can help to make other sounds besides "l" in *loo, lee, lah*. The tongue helps to make "t" and "d." We remember that it peeked out between the teeth when we said "th." Ask the children to show their teeth (white gates) and to close and open them. Emphasize the fact that "l" is prolonged and that we use our voice box.

DOGGIE'S TONGUE

Lap, lap, lap, lap, lap,
    Goes my doggie's tongue
    When he takes a drink.
Lap, lap, lap, lap, lap,
    The water is gone
    Quicker than a wink.

The "laps" should be made rapidly on a second repetition of the jingle in order to imitate the doggie drinking water. The first repetition should emphasize the correct placement of the tongue.

LEAVES

I like leaves . . . all kinds of leaves:
Gay little red leaves,
Sad little brown leaves,
Happy little green leaves,
Sunny little yellow leaves.
I like leaves . . . all kinds of leaves.

Use the magic flannel board to tell this jingle with the class. Cut out leaves and place them on the flannel board when they are mentioned in the jingle. Other colors besides the ones mentioned may be used. Children may choose adjectives to describe the colors. Have each child come to the front of the room and select a leaf to put on the flannel board, saying: "I like——leaves" as they do so.

This device can be used for drill on the "r" sound which appears in the names of these colors: red, green, orange, brown, purple, silver, and gray.

CLOWNS

A clown is very funny.
He wears such funny clothes.
     (Refrain)   La, la, lee,
                  He wears such funny clothes.

He has a funny mouth
Beneath a funny nose.
     (Refrain)   La, la, lee,
                  Beneath a funny nose.

Some clowns are very tall,
And some are very fat.
     (Refrain)   La, la, lee,
                  And some are very fat.

And where the hair should be
Is a funny little hat.
     (Refrain)   La, la, lee,
                  Is a funny little hat.

Clowns wear enormous shoes
That flip-flop up and down.
     (Refrain)   La, la, lee,
                  That flip-flop up and down.

It's fun to be so funny;
I think I'll be a clown.
     (Refrain)   La, la, lee,
                  I think I'll be a clown.

This poem may be used with solo parts, group refrains, two groups, or as unison work with an individual doing the refrain.

The Letter Game

Place in an envelope a picture of an object containing the "l" sound or any other sound a particular child may be trying to correct. The child then says:

> "Mr. Postman, please look in your bag and see
> If you have a letter, a letter for me."

When the child opens his envelope, he says, "My letter has a picture of a lamb, lamp, bell, ball, etc."

LUCY LOST HER LOCKET

1st group: Lucy, Lucy,
I have heard
That you lost your locket
In my backyard.

2nd group: Lucy, Lucy,
Did you look
To see if your locket
Fell into the brook?

3rd group: Lucy, Lucy,
Come and see,
Maybe your locket
Is in the tree.

4th group: Lucy, Lucy,
Look over there.
I see your locket
Under a chair.

BALLOONS

Eight balloons . . . I'll sell them to you,
Red and yellow and green and blue,
Orange ones, and brown ones, and purple ones, too;
And here are the black ones . . . I'll sell them to you.

Who will buy my blue balloon, as blue as the heaven?
Take it away . . . now there are seven.
Who will buy my brown balloon, brown like many sticks?
Take it away . . . now there are six.
Who will buy my red balloon, a color so alive?
Take it away . . . now there are five.
Who will buy my purple balloon, there are not many
    more?
Take it away . . . now there are four.
Who will buy my green balloon, as green as a tree?
Take it away . . . now there are three.
Who will buy my orange balloon? An orange is good
    for you.
Take it away . . . now there are two.
Who will buy my yellow balloon, as yellow as the sun?
Take it away . . . now there is one.
Who will buy my black balloon? Now we are done.
Take it away . . . now there is none.

    Prepare large balloons of colored paper, and on the question "who
will buy" select a child to "take it away." Use the paper balloons in the
manner of flash cards. Children call out the color as a balloon is held up.

The Balloon Game

Place the colored paper balloons used in the poem above in a large envelope with the strings hanging out. A child is invited to choose a balloon of any color he may wish. He takes one of the strings and pulls out his balloon. If the balloon is the same color as the one he chose, he wins another turn and a chance to select a balloon of another color. Drill on the "l" sound is provided as the child says, "I choose a (red) balloon."

LISTENING

Let me hear the little wind blowing in the trees,
    "wh...wh...wh..."
Let me hear the humming sound of the busy bees,
    "zzzzzzzzzz."
Let me hear the teakettle when it's making steam,
    "ssssssssssssss."
Let me hear the Jersey cow in the meadow green,
    "mmmmm...oooooo..."
Let me hear the rooster as he flaps his wings,
    "r, r, r, r, r."
Let me hear the little girl as this song she sings:
    "La, la, la, la, la."

The class may repeat the first three words of each line ("Let me hear") with the teacher and then join in on each refrain.

The last refrain may be carried over into a tune which the class knows, using "la-la-la" in place of words.

The "s," "z," and "r" sounds are also given drill in this poem.

BALLOON FINGERS

One finger I have and that's a balloon,
    a red balloon.
Two fingers I have and they are balloons,
    a red balloon and a green balloon.
Three fingers I have and they are balloons,
    a red balloon, a green balloon, and
    a blue balloon.

Have circles of colored paper attached to a paper ring band to fit over a finger tip. As many balloons as desired can be used, each of a different color. Decrease fingers in the same way.

WHAT THEY SAY

Class: Little white cat, little white cat,
    What do you say?
Solo 1: I say, "Mew, mew, pitty-pat-pat."
Class: Little gray mouse, little gray mouse,
    What do you say?
Solo 2: I say, "Squeak, squeak, all through the house."
Class: Little green frog, little green frog,
    What do you say?
Solo 3: I say, "Glug, glug, sitting on a log."
Class: Little brown squirrel, little brown squirrel,
    What do you say?
Solo: I say, "Chatter-chee, with my tail in a curl."
Class: Little black pig, little black pig,
    What do you say?
Solo: I say, "Oink, oink, as I wallow and dig."

The teacher should use animal pictures to stimulate class responses. The tongue sound "l" is repeated in the word *little*. The child who has learned to make the "s," "ch," and "g," should be given an opportunity to do a solo part and thus have a successful experience.

Speech Reading and Pantomime

Whisper the sentences softly so that the children will read the sound formations on the lips. Before the game starts, the teacher should show the placement of "l" with the tongue and tell the children that they will see the sound in each thing she asks them to do. The exercise is used principally for visual discrimination. The class may act out the sentences singly or in the group.

Blink your eyes.	Lift something.
Go to sleep.	Clap your hands.
Fold your hands.	Look at me.
Climb a ladder.	Close the door.
Look at the floor.	Look at the class.
Point to the wall.	Point to the blackboard.
Look at the ceiling.	Fold your hands.
Look at the light.	Sit up tall.

Grocery Store Game

Children think of products with the "l" sound which may be purchased at a grocery store. As a child has a turn, he says, "I like to buy——at the grocery store."

Children may choose lettuce, celery, lamb, liver, oleomargarine, milk, plums, salt, pickles, apples, etc.

Jungle Game

One child says, "I saw a lion in the jungle." The next child adds an animal, insect, bird, or any living thing to what the first child has said. The third child adds to the first and second observations. The thing being seen, however, must contain the "l" sound. This game will also serve as excellent memory drill.

leopard	owl	antelope	butterfly
lizard	wolf	caterpillar	alligator
turtle	fly	squirrel	elephant
llama	oriole	glowworm	camel
eagle	lion	firefly	gorilla

"l" *Sound Game*

Have a series of objects, small toys, or pictures that contain the "l" sound. As the child chooses an object or a picture, he will say, "I choose a lamb," or "I choose a ball," whatever the item happens to be. The teacher should pay close attention to the production of the "l."

A SPRING STORY

This is a story to use on the magic flannel board. Secure or draw the necessary objects or animals mentioned in the story. As you place them on the board, the children will say the repeated words with you to get drill on "l."

In April we see a blue, blue sky.

In the blue, blue sky there are fluffy, fluffy clouds in the month of April.

Here is a green, green lawn under the fluffy, fluffy clouds in the blue, blue sky in the month of April.

Now we plant a tall, tall tree on the green, green lawn under the fluffy, fluffy clouds in the blue, blue sky in the month of April.

See the leafy, leafy leaves on the tall, tall tree on the green, green lawn under the fluffy, fluffy clouds in the blue, blue sky in the month of April.

Here we plant some yellow, yellow daffodils on the green, green lawn under the tall, tall tree with the leafy, leafy leaves under the fluffy, fluffy clouds in the blue, blue sky in the month of April.

Let us plant purple, purple violets near the yellow, yellow daffodils on the green, green lawn under the tall, tall tree with the leafy, leafy leaves under the fluffy, fluffy clouds in the blue, blue sky in the month of April.

Additional animals and objects can be added for "l" drill: woolly, woolly sheep, Little Boy Blue, curly, curly dog, etc.

When all of the objects have been placed on the board, the teacher may say the following poem, or the children may say it in unison.

SPRING SONG

I love the Spring;
 The grass is green.
  Such colors I
   Have never seen.

I love the Spring;
 Especially May,
  When little bugs
   Come out to play.

I love the Spring;
 The air is sweet,
  And everything
   Has dancing feet
    In lovely Spring.

114

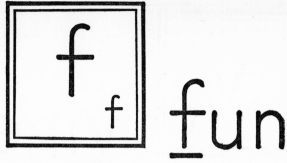

Making the Sound:

The upper teeth are pressed lightly against the lower lip and the air is forced out between the teeth and the lip. The soft palate is raised and there is no vibration of the vocal cords.

The "f" sound is sometimes misarticulated as "p" or voiceless "th"; i. e., *pour* or *thour* instead of *four*.

Call "f" the—

Cross kitten sound

Correcting the Sound:

Ask the child to bite his lower lip gently and blow out his breath at the same time. A mirror will help the child see the correct teeth-lip position. By observing his image in the mirror and watching the teacher make a correct "f" sound, he will soon be able to produce the sound himself.

Words:

Initial	*Medial*	*Final*
feather	elephant	calf
five	telephone	knife
finger	coffee	laugh

Blends:

"fl"–flat	"fr"–frog	"rf"–scarf	"lf"–elf
fly	fruit	dwarf	wolf

115

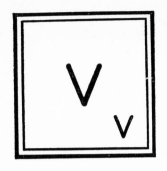

V v v̱ine

Making the Sound:

This sound is made like the "f" sound, except that the vocal cords vibrate.

The "v" sound is frequently misarticulated in the speech of children with Spanish-American backgrounds. "b" is the usual substitution, i. e., *balentine* and *seben* for *valentine* and *seven*.

Call "v" the—

Fly sound

Correcting the Sound:

Use the same techniques as outlined for the "f" sound. Direct contrast between the "v" and the "f" sounds will help develop the "v." Have the children feel the vibrations in the nose and the voice box as the sound is made.

| veal – feel | vine – fine | vast – fast |
| vase – face | have – half | save – safe |

Words:

Initial	*Medial*	*Final*
valentine	seven	glove
vase	eleven	stove
violet	envelope	five

116

CROSS KITTEN

Teacher: "f" is the sound Fuzzy Kitten makes. Touch your lower lip with your upper teeth. Now blow gently with your breath. "f" is called the "cross kitten" sound because a kitten says "f" when he is cross, or angry, or frightened.

Kitten puts her back up high,
"f, f, f,"
When our collie passes by;
"f, f, f."
She fluffs her tail and says: "Meow,
'f, f, f,' "
And causes quite a dreadful row,
"f, f, f."

FUZZY

Fuzzy is a kitten,
Nice and soft and fat.
Fuzzy plays with Susan;
Feet go pitter pat.
Fuzzy's tail is fluffy;
Face is clean and yet,
Fuzzy has no washcloth;
Funny Fuzzy pet.

Ask the children to listen for the words that have the "cross kitten" sound. They may raise their hands upon recognition of the words as the teacher reads the poem.

funny   fat   fuzzy   feet   fluffy   face

FINGER PLAY

Fee, fie, foe, fum;
See the little brownie run.
Fee, fie, foe, fum;
Four fingers having fun.
Fee, fie, foe, fum;
My brownie is a little

Thumb.

Have the children close their fists and make a finger pop up each time "fee, fie, foe, fum" is said. The thumb wiggles each time the "brownie" is mentioned. This exercise differentiates between the "f" in *fum* and the "th" in *thumb*.

LITTLE JACK PUMPKIN FACE

Little Jack Pumpkin Face
Lives on a vine.
Little Jack Pumpkin Face
Thinks that is fine.
First, he is small and green,
Then big and yellow;
Little Jack Pumpkin Face,
Funny little fellow.

—Adapted from a country rhyme

Point out the difference between "f" and "v." The sounds are made alike, except that "v" is voiced and "f" is voiceless. Words having the "f" sound in the poem are:

| face | first | fellow | funny | fine |

118

I WENT TO THE FARM

I went to the farm, and I saw a duck.

The duck said, "Quack, quack."

I went to the farm, and I saw a cat.

The cat said, "Meow, meow";

The duck said, "Quack, quack."

I went to the farm, and I saw a lamb.

The lamb said, "Baa, baa";

The cat said, "Meow, meow";

The duck said, "Quack, quack."

Other farm animals and the sounds they make may be substituted or added: "Maa" for the goat, "r-r-r-r-r" for the rooster, etc. Pictures should be used to help children remember the animals in their order.

Matching Pictures Game

The teacher gives an incomplete sentence and the child selects a picture to complete it. Ask the children to listen for the "cross kitten" sound in each of the picture words.

An animal with a long neck is called a . . . . . . giraffe.

When we cut food, we use a . . . . knife.

It swims in the water and it is called a . . . . fish.

We take food to our mouth and we use a . . . . . . fork.

We wear rings on our . . . . fingers.

An animal with a trunk is called an . . . . elephant.

A baby cow is called a . . . . calf.

It grows on the branch of a tree and it is called a . leaf.

It grows in the garden and it is called a . . . . . . flower.

FLUFFY KITTEN

Ask the children to join in each time the story says: "Fluffy humped up her back, and fluffed out her tail, and said, 'f...f...f...'" Use the magic flannel board to help tell the story. As Fluffy meets the animals and the bird, place pictures of them on the board. Have pictures of Fluffy and Susie, also.

Susie was a little girl who lived in a large city, right next to a big park. Sometimes Susie got very lonely. She wanted someone to play with her, and so one evening Daddy brought home a little kitten. Susie promptly named the kitten Fluffy.

Susie soon learned that Fluffy had a language all her own. When Fluffy was happy, she sang, "Purr...purr ...purr..." When she was hungry, she cried, "Mew, mew, mew." And when she wanted to go out or come inside she always said, "Me-ow, me-ow, me-ow."

Sometimes Fluffy became frightened or cross. Then *she would hump up her back, fluff out her tail, and say, "f...f...f..."* Her lip curled up and her tail looked like a big powder puff. I am sure that you have all heard a kitten make that sound: "f...f...f..."

One day, while Fluffy was exploring her new yard, she discovered a hole in the fence. Being a curious little kitten, she crawled through and found herself in a place with lots of lawn and trees. At one side of the lawn she saw a little lake. Fluffy did not know it, but she was in the big park next door to Susie's house.

Fluffy decided to look around this beautiful spot. She had not gone far, however, when she heard a chitter-chatter behind her. She turned her head, and there she saw a very strange animal. Of course, it was only a

120

squirrel, but Fluffy had never seen a squirrel. She became frightened. *So she humped up her back, fluffed out her tail, and said, "f...f...f..."*

Now the squirrel never had seen a kitten before, nor had it heard such an angry sound as "f . . . f . . . f . . ." It frightened the squirrel, and scamper, scamper he went, up a tree.

Fluffy hurried across the lawn, away from the strange animal, but as she went around a tree, she saw a big blue bird right in front of her. Fluffy had never seen a bird before and she was frightened. *So she humped up her back, fluffed out her tail, and said, "f...f...f..."*

The bird, however, knew all about cats, and it went flitter-flutter, up into a tree.

By this time, Fluffy had had enough of this beautiful spot with the strange animals, but when she looked around for her fence with the hole, it was no longer in sight. Fluffy was lost.

Unhappy Fluffy said, "Me-ow, me-ow, me-ow," with a very sad voice. "How can I find my way home?" Through the park she went, looking for the fence with the hole in it.

But Fluffy's troubles were not over. Across the lawn came a big brown dog, out for a romp with his master. The dog saw Fluffy just as Fluffy saw him. My, how frightened Fluffy was. *She humped up her back, fluffed out her tail, and said, "f...f...f...,"* but the dog just kept coming. This time it was Fluffy that went scramble, scramble up a tree.

The dog's master came along, put the leash back on

the dog's neck, and off they went. But Fluffy in the tree was much too frightened to come down, and besides it was beginning to get dark. Maybe she could call loudly enough for Susie to hear. She opened her little pink mouth to make a loud me-ow when she saw a happy sight. There was Susie, coming through the trees, calling, "Here, Fluffy, Fluffy, Fluffy."

Fluffy called back with a loud "Me-ow, me-ow, me-ow." Susie heard the kitten and came over to the tree to help her down. She held the frightened little kitten gently in her arms. Soon, Fluffy stopped trembling and began to feel happy once more. Susie looked down at Fluffy and she heard a contented little "Purr...purr... purr..."

And all the while, Fluffy was hoping that never again would she have to *hump up her back, fluff out her tail, and say, "f...f...f..."* in such an angry way. It was so much nicer to feel contented and happy.

The "v" Sound

Teacher: You can feel "v" in your voice box. Your upper teeth touch your lower lip gently as you say: "vvvvvvvvv." Feel the sound as you say the words: *valentine, vine, move,* and *give.*

Vee, vie, voo, voe;
Upper teeth to lip must go.
"f," says kitten,
"v," says fly;
You can feel them
If you try.
Vee, vie, voo, voe;
Upper teeth to lip must go.

GREEN FLY

The little green fly
Can do tricks like a clown.
"vvvvvv"
He can walk on the ceiling
Without falling down.
"vvvvvv"
His tiny green wings
Take him round and around,
"vvvvvv"
Like a plane in the sky,
As he drones a wee sound.
"vvvvvv"

VALENTINES

Valentines, valentines,
How many do I see?
Valentines, valentines,
Share them with me.

1st child: I have red ones.
2nd child: I have orange ones.
3rd child: I have yellow ones, too.
4th child: I have green ones.
5th child: I have purple ones.
6th child: I have some that are blue.

Valentines, valentines,
How many do I see?
Valentines, valentines,
Count them with me:
1 - 2 - 3 - 4 - 5 - 6.

This jingle lends itself readily to the magic flannel board. Note the "v" sound in *valentines, have,* and the number *five.*

Did you ever see an elephant sitting in a tree?
Did you ever see a rooster swimming in the sea?

All: Never; no, never; no, never!

Did you ever see a monkey striped all pink and
   black?
Did you ever see a cat with green spots upon his
   back?

All: Never; no, never; no, never!

Did you ever see a dog holding doughnuts on his
   tail?
Did you ever see the postman bring milk instead of
   mail?

All: Never; no, never; no, never!

Let children think up similar impossible situations. Have them say
"Did you ever," and let the class chorus "Never; no, never; no, never."

Games for the "v" Sound

1. Collect small toys for a surprise box. The child
opens the box, takes out a toy, and says, "I have a . . ."
This serves as practice for the final "v" sound, as in *have*.

2. Cut out small pictures of objects and paste them
on red paper hearts. As the child chooses a heart, he says,
"My valentine has a picture of . . ." Practice is gained for
the initial "v" in *valentine* and the final "v" sound in *of*.

3. Using paper of various colors, cut out five small
circles of each color and paste them on a large sheet of
cardboard. The child counts the circles and says, "I counted
five red circles, I counted five blue circles," etc. Although
emphasis is upon the "f" and "v" sounds, as in *five*, exercise is given on the "s" sound, as in *circle*.

124

VEE VEE, THE FLY

Explain to the children that they are to join in each time the "fly" sound, "vvvvvv," is heard in the story. Glance around the class whenever the children are chorusing Vee Vee's song to make certain that the "v" sound is being made with the upper teeth touching their lower lips.

Vee Vee was a tiny fly. He had shiny green wings and when the sun shone on them, they looked like something a fairy had made.

Vee Vee had a voice and he liked to use it. You could hear him humming "vvvvvv" almost any time during the day. In the evening, he slept on the ceiling high above the floor. On his feet was a sticky glue that he made himself, and that is what kept him from falling off the ceiling. He said "vvvvvv" loudly when he wanted to get out through a crack in the door, and "vvvvvv" very fast when someone drove him away from the food.

Vee Vee enjoyed zooming around the room making his "vvvvvv" sound. He would sit for a second, make believe he was an airplane, and take off with a "vvvvvv."

In fact, he looked a great deal like an airplane, for he had wings, and he could dive and land and move in any direction. It was fun to watch him, for you never knew what Vee Vee was going to do next. But of this anyone could be sure . . . Vee Vee's song was always "vvvvvv" and he behaved just like any other little green fly.

"vvvvvv,"
Around the room.
"vvvvvv,"
Watch him zoom:
Vee Vee, the little green fly.

125

she

Making the Sound:

The sides of the tongue are pressed against the teeth while the body of the tongue is arched toward the hard palate. The lips are protruded and tend to be squared rather than rounded. The air is forced out between the tongue and the palate. Teeth are only slightly apart. The soft palate is raised and the vocal cords do not vibrate.

"sh" is one of the consonant sounds most commonly defective.

Call "sh" the—
Still sound
Hush sound
Rushing water sound

Correcting the Sound:

This sound is often misarticulated because a child tends to retract his lips into a smile instead of protruding them in a relatively squared position. Let the child observe closely the correct placement for this sound; then let him practice with a mirror. Provide ear training repeatedly.

If the teacher will demonstrate and explain why this sound is called the "still" or "hush" sound, and then use it in words, some children will be helped to make it through imitation.

The teacher should stress the fact that "sh" is a continuant in order to distinguish it from the often substituted "ch" sound which is explosive in quality.

WORDS:

Initial	*Medial*	*Final*
sheep	fishing	wash
shoes	dishes	dish
shell	seashore	fish

BLENDS:

"shr"–shrub	"sht"–mashed
shrink	pushed

 measure

MAKING THE SOUND:

This sound is made like the "sh" sound, except that
the vocal cords vibrate. The "zh" sound is one of the last
that is acquired by a child in his normal speech development. It is also one of the consonant sounds most frequently defective.

Call "zh" the—

Hair clippers sound

Vacuum cleaner sound

CORRECTING THE SOUND:

Correction should follow the technique for the "sh" sound. Have the children feel the difference between "zh" and "sh" by placing their hands on the voice boxes.

WORDS:

Medial	*Final*
pleasure	garage
explosion	mirage
treasure	corsage
usual	rouge

POEM ABOUT A SOUND

This is a poem about a sound:
Our lips are squared and nearly round.
Our tongue must help, our teeth do, too,
So I take a good breath and the sound comes through:
"sh ... sh ... sh ... sh ..."
> "sh ..." as in shoe, and "sh ..." as in fish,
> "sh ..." as in ship, and "sh ..." as in dish.

Everyone looks at his feet,
And there he sees so nicely neat:
Black shoes and white shoes,
Buckle, tie, and button shoes.
> "sh ..." as in shoe, and "sh ..." as in fish,
> "sh ..." as in ship, and "sh ..." as in dish.

Goldfish swimming in a bowl,
Whatever would you do
If in your bowl there was a hole,
And the water all came through?
> "sh ..." as in shoe, and "sh ..." as in fish,
> "sh ..." as in ship, and "sh ..." as in dish.

I saw a ship a-sailing
Away out on the sea.
I sent a wish out to that ship
To sail back home to me.
>"sh . . ." as in shoe, and "sh . . ." as in fish,
>"sh . . ." as in ship, and "sh . . ." as in dish.

Here is a rhyme about a dish,
A dish without a spoon.
A dish with a cat, a cat with a fiddle,
And a cow jumped over the moon.
>"sh . . ." as in shoe, and "sh . . ." as in fish,
>"sh . . ." as in ship, and "sh . . ." as in dish.

Have mounted pictures of a shoe, a fish, a ship, and a dish. Use them as flash cards. Whenever it is time for the child to say the word, hold up the picture that corresponds to it.

The Wishing Game

Let children state their wishes concerning what they would like to do during the summer or other vacation period, what they would like to eat, what they would like to receive for Christmas or for a birthday, etc. Each child should state his wish with these words: "I wish for . . ." This is a fine drill for the "sh" sound in the final position.

129

SKATING

Let us go skating over the ice,
All: Swish, swish, swish.
The air is crisp and the weather is nice,
All: Swish, swish, swish.
My skates are bright and shiny and new,
All: Swish, swish, swish.
I have a warm scarf and some woolly socks, too,
All: Swish, swish, swish.
Let us go skating over the ice,
All: Swish, swish, swish.
And what if we do fall once or twice?
All: Swish, swish, swish.

In the refrain, children will get drill on the final "sh" sound and the "sw" blend.

FISHING

I went to fish down by the brook,
And not one fish would take my hook.
I wished and wished with all my might,
But wishing would not make them bite.
When they could not be caught, I knew
The fishes did some wishing, too.

The medial and final "sh" sounds are illustrated in this poem. See the chapter on "Devices to Use with This Book" for instructions on making a fishing game to use in conjunction with this poem or as a separate device for teaching phonics. Place words with the "sh" sound in them on the cardboard fish which are used in the game.

MY HEN

I had a little hen, the prettiest ever seen.
She was, she was the prettiest ever seen.
She washed the dishes and she kept the house clean.
She washed, she washed, and she kept the house clean.
She went to the mill to get me some flour.
She went, she went to get me some flour.
She brought it home in less than an hour.
She brought it, she brought it in less than an hour.
She baked me some bread and she made me some tea.
She baked, she baked, and she made me some tea.
She sat by the fire and she told tales to me.
She sat, she sat, and she told tales to me.

—Adapted from Mother Goose

Lines 1, 3, 5, 7, 9, and 11 are solo lines, while the even numbered
lines are to be said by the group.

131

MACHINES

"sh . . . sh . . . sh . . ."
        Washing machine.
"sh . . . sh . . . sh . . ."
        Clothes are clean.

"ch, ch, ch,"
        Threshing grain.
Threshing machine
        Sounds like train.

"zh . . . zh . . . zh . . ."
        Mowing machine;
Cutting grass
        Growing green.

"th . . . th . . . th . . ." (Voiced)
        Humming low;
Sewing machine,
        Hear it go.

Whirr . . . whirr . . . whirr . . .
        Mixing cake;
Master mixer,
        Now we'll bake.

"z . . . z . . . z . . ."
        Motor machine;
Elevator,
        Floor sixteen.

The word *machine* has the medial "sh" sound.

Sound Recognition

Hold up pictures containing the "sh" sound and say the pictured objects for the children. Tell them that "sh" is sometimes at the beginning, at the middle, or at the end of a word.

The child asks for a picture saying, "Will you please show me a picture of a toothbrush (shovel, dish, etc.)?"

The teacher answers, "Surely. Is the 'sh' sound at the beginning? In the middle? At the end?"

The child then gives the proper response. Pictures obtainable from magazines are:

dishes	sheep	washing machine
shovel	shells	salt shaker
shoes	radish	ash can
ship	ocean	shed
shawl	seashore	sugar bowl
fish	bushes	toothbrush

Cash Register Game

Have the children make play money and put it into a box. Each child has a turn taking pennies, nickels, or dimes from the box and saying: "I will put three pennies into the cash register"; "I will put a dime into the cash register"; etc. This gives the child practice on the two sounds, "sh" and "j."

Dish Game

A set of toy dishes is necessary for this game. The child sets a table with the dishes, naming each one as he puts it into place: "This dish is a plate. This dish is a saucer," etc. Pictures may be used instead of actual dishes.

Monday Wash

Cut pictures of articles of clothing from magazines and reinforce them with cardboard. Place them in a box. As a child draws out a picture, he says: "I did my washing last Monday." The teacher asks: "What did you wash?" The child's answer should correspond to the picture that he has drawn: "I washed some socks"; "I washed a dress"; etc.

THE SEASHELL

The teacher puts her finger to her lips each time she wishes the children to say the "still" sound which appears frequently in the story. Each verse is repeated once so that children may catch the words from the teacher and join in as she tells it. The Seashell story is also a good medium for relaxation.

One day at the beach the wind blew and blew and blew. The ocean waves dashed high on the rocks, swish, shirr, swish, shirr.

A little seashell, who lived at the bottom of the ocean, was awakened from his sleep.

"Oh, dear," he cried fearfully, "what is happening?"

The ocean tossed him back and forth, back and forth, until he was out of breath. Then it spilled him right on the beach and there he lay almost afraid to move. At last the wind became still. The sun shone brightly and warmed the little seashell. The breeze sang a lullaby:

> " 'sh ... sh ... sh ... ,' little seashell
> From your ocean bed;
> You are in a new land now,
> So rest your weary head.
> 'sh ... sh ... sh ...' "

The ocean whispered softly:

"'sh . . . sh . . . sh . . . ,' little seashell
From your ocean bed;
You are in a new land now,
So rest your weary head.
'sh . . . sh . . . sh . . .' "

The sun said not a word but shone radiantly, and soon the little seashell was cozy and fast asleep.

All at once he was rudely awakened. He felt himself snatched up and tossed across the beach. A noisy boy cried, "It is just an old seashell. It is not worth anything."

The ocean whispered:

"'sh . . . sh . . . sh . . . ,' little seashell,
Just lie very still;
'sh . . . sh . . . sh . . .'
You can, if you will.

The breeze whispered:

"'sh . . . sh . . . sh . . . ,' little seashell,
Just lie very still;
'sh . . . sh . . . sh . . .'
You can, if you will.

A tired little boy came to where the seashell was lying. The little boy was crying, "I want my mother and daddy. I am lost."

The seashell was sorry for the tired little boy.

"Maybe if I whisper the 'still' sound, the tired little boy will hear me," he thought.

So he whispered, "sh...sh...sh..."

The tired little boy stopped crying and looked all around to see where the quiet sound was coming from.

Then he saw the seashell.

"What a pretty seashell," he said.

"sh...sh...sh...," whispered the seashell.

"And what a pretty sound," said the tired little boy.

He held the seashell close to his ear.

"sh...sh...sh...," it whispered softly.

Then the tired little boy's mother and daddy came along. They were so happy to find their boy.

The seashell kept right on whispering, "sh...sh... sh..." as the tired little boy held him in a hand that was very limp. In fact, all of the tired little boy was limp, for he was fast asleep. Then they all went home, mother, daddy, the tired little boy, and the seashell.

All day and night the seashell lay on the toy shelf and sang the song that the ocean and the breeze had taught him. You can sing it, too, and I promise you that if you will sing it often enough, everything and everybody around you will be as still as "sh...sh...sh..."

WHAT THE VACUUM CLEANER SAYS

"zh..................,"
The vacuum cleaner hums.
"zh....................,"
He picks up all the crumbs.
"zh....................,"
He slides across the floor.
"zh....................,"
He glides from door to door.
"zh...................."

CUTTING HAIR

"zh...zh...zh..."
The clippers go over my hair,
As I sit up straight
In the barber chair.
"zh...zh...zh..."
Be careful, little Bill,
For we cannot cut it straight,
If you do not sit still.
"zh...zh...zh..."
Make a big deep bow;
Hair is cut short;
You're a big boy, now.

MEASURING

I measure from head clear down to my toes;
I measure my arm and even my nose.
I measure my legs, my chest, and all.
I measure to see if I have grown tall.

137

Treasure Box

To get practice on the "sh" and "zh" sounds, use a box with a hinged lid which contains pictures of articles having the sounds. The child opens the box and says: "I found a——in my treasure chest."

Garage Game

Mount pictures of different makes of automobiles on colored paper. Many children are familiar with types of cars and can easily tell the difference between them. Use a makeshift garage (an ordinary box will do) and have each child put a car or cars into the "garage." Be sure that the child pronounces the "zh" in the word *garage* as he says, "I put my——car into the garage."

THE VACUUM CLEANER

Show that the "vacuum cleaner" sound is made like the "still" sound, except that we can feel it, as we make it, in our voice boxes. The teacher cues the children when it is time to make the sound.

A vacuum cleaner sat far back in the mop closet. Mr. Brown had bought him weeks ago so that the house would be nice and clean. For a time the vacuum made a quiet hum . . . "zhzhzhzhzhzhzh" . . . and suddenly his insides hurt. When Mrs. Brown took him out of the closet and hooked him up to the wall socket, he said "zhzhzhzh-zhzhzh" so loudly that it frightened her.

"I cannot use such a noisy vacuum cleaner," cried Mrs. Brown. "It makes a noise so loud that it will bother all of the neighbors."

"Let me try," said Mr. Brown. So he pushed the switch.

"zhzhzhzhzhzhzh," went the vacuum cleaner loudly.

"Oh, dear," sighed Mr. Brown. "Perhaps I had better take this vacuum cleaner back to the store."

But he put the vacuum cleaner back into the mop closet and forgot all about it. Mrs. Brown had to use the broom, and the air was always filled with dust and the rugs were not clean at all.

The vacuum cleaner was not happy because he wanted to be working. Besides, he was hungry. His bag had not a speck of dust or dirt in it. And he still had a pain, too.

All at once he felt a trickle . . . trickle . . . trickle. Mr. Brown had put an oil can on the closet shelf and it was leaking all over the vacuum cleaner's feet. Some of the oil seeped through the door and Mrs. Brown saw it. When she opened the closet door, she saw the oil all over the floor of the closet.

"Come here, Mr. Brown," she said. "That old oil can is leaking on the floor of the closet. Now the vacuum cleaner is ruined and you can't take it back to the store."

Mr. Brown said, "We'll just have to use it now, noise or no noise." So he hooked the vacuum cleaner up to the wall socket again.

"zhzhzhzhzh," hummed the vacuum cleaner quietly . . . "zhzhzhzhzhzhzhzhzhzh."

"Well, did you ever . . . ," exclaimed Mrs. Brown.

"Well, did you ever . . . ," exclaimed Mr. Brown. "I do believe that all the vacuum cleaner needed was a good oiling."

And of course, he was right.

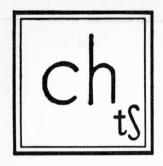 <u>ch</u>oose

Making the Sound:

This sound is a combination of "t" and "sh." In making it, the tongue, lips, and teeth move rapidly from the "t" to the "sh" position. The tongue is pressed firmly against the entire gum ridge, holding the air inside the mouth. As the tongue assumes the position for "sh," the air is released suddenly and explosively as the "ch" sound. The lips become squared and protruded. The soft palate is raised and the vocal cords do not vibrate.

"ch" is one of the least used of the consonant sounds, but is one of the most commonly misarticulated.

Call "ch" the—

Train or engine sound

Sneeze sound

Correcting the Sound:

The error usually heard here is a substitution of "sh" for "ch," i. e., *shair* for *chair, shoes* for *choose*. It is the combination of the "t" and "sh" sounds that causes difficulty. Occasionally the air may slip around the edges of the tongue to give a cloudy effect similar to a lateral lisp.

Have the children imitate a sneeze. This will give the feeling of the "t" and "sh" combination. Imitating the "ch-ch-ch-ch" of a train engine may also help in producing the sound. Ear training and word differentiation drills should be provided.

shoe	– chew		dish	– ditch
ship	– chip		wish	– witch
sheep	– cheap		cash	– catch
shin	– chin		crush	– crutch

WORDS:

Initial	*Medial*	*Final*
chair	kitchen	church
cheese	pitcher	watch
chicken	teacher	lunch

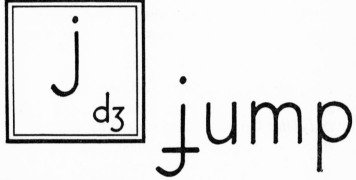

MAKING THE SOUND:

This sound is made like the "ch" sound, except that the vocal cords vibrate. It is a combination of "d" and "zh," with the speech organs moving from the "d" position to the "zh" position.

"j" is one of the least common of the consonant sounds in frequency of use, but is one of the most frequently defective sounds.

Call "j" the—

Jumping Jack sound

Correcting the Sound:

If the "ch" sound is defective, the "j" sound is also likely to be. Have the child say "d"; then "zh"; then "d" and "zh" in rapid succession. One hand should be on the voice box in order to feel the vibrations. Ear training is important. Sound differentiation drills will help.

Jane	– chain	joke	– choke
Jill	– chill	jug	– chug
Joyce	– choice	jump	– chump

Words:

Initial	Medial	Final
juice	soldier	bridge
jump	gingerbread	badge
jam	fire engine	orange

CHOO CHOO TRAIN

1st child: Listen to the choo choo train,
All: "ch, ch, ch-ch-ch,"
2nd child: Go down the track and back again,
All: "ch, ch, ch-ch-ch."
3rd child: Sometimes fast, sometimes slow,
All: "ch, ch, ch-ch-ch,"
4th child: It takes you where you want to go,
All: "ch, ch, ch-ch-ch."
5th child: Now it's chugging up a hill!
All: "CH, CH, CH-CH-CH!"
6th child: Now it's stopping, Whoa Bill,
All: "ch, ch, ch-ch-ch,
         ch, ch, ch-ch-ch, *(softer)*
         ch, ch, ch-ch-ch." *(softer still)*

—CONRAD WEDBERG

THE SURPRISE

Solo: Robin Redbreast sat in a tree,
All:　　　Chee, chee, chee,
　　　　　Chee, chee, chee,
Solo: Singing a happy song to me.
All:　　　Chee, chee, chee,
　　　　　Chee, chee, chee.
Solo: "Surprise, surprise," he seemed to say,
All:　　　Chee, chee, chee,
　　　　　Chee, chee, chee.
Solo: "My mate is hatching some eggs today."
All:　　　Chee, chee, chee,
　　　　　Chee, chee, chee.
Solo: I'll tell you a secret, if you won't tell:
　　　　Four baby robins popped out of the shell.
　　　　I sat just as quiet as quiet could be,
　　　　As Robin sang, "Chee, chee-chee, chee-chee."

WOODCUTTER'S SONG

All: "Chop, chop, chop, chop,"
      That is the woodcutter's song.
Solo: He swings the axe
      That cuts the wood
      That feeds the fire
      That cooks the food.
All: "Chop, chop, chop, chop,"
      That is the woodcutter's song.

Rhythmic repetition of the word *chop* will add to the visual imagery of the poem.

"I Choose" Game

This game is based upon the song "Old MacDonald Had a Farm." Mount pictures of farm fowls and animals on flannel for use on the magic flannel board.

To start the game, have a child select an animal or fowl, saying as he does so, "I choose a duck; the duck says, 'Quack, quack,' " "I choose a turkey; the turkey says, 'Gobble, gobble,' " etc. He places his choice on the magic flannel board and the class then sings the stanza of the song about his animal or fowl. The game may continue as long as the teacher wishes.

CHEE-CHEE-A-ROO

Teacher: Each morning when the sun comes up,
I feel just like a bird.
I sing and sing a happy song;
It's something I have heard.

Children: Chee-chee-chee-a-ree,
Chee-chee-chee-a-roo,
Chee-a-ree, chee-a-roo,
Chee-a-ree-a-roo.

Teacher: I don't know where I heard the song,
Or how it came to be;
Unless the robin made it up
Especially for me.

Children: Chee-chee-chee-a-ree,
Chee-chee-chee-a-roo,
Chee-a-ree, chee-a-roo,
Chee-a-ree-a-roo.

Teacher: I like to sing chee-chee-a-roo,
Because I feel so gay,
And people want to listen to
My cheerful song all day.

Children: Chee-chee-chee-a-ree,
Chee-chee-chee-a-roo,
Chee-a-ree, chee-a-roo,
Chee-a-ree-a-roo.

CHITTER CHATTER

The children chorus the refrain which Chitter Chatter speaks each time he meets a character in the story. The class may also act out the story with stick or paper bag puppets. Instruct children to listen for words that have the "train engine" sound.

Chitter Chatter, the squirrel, was a busy little fellow. He could run up a tree faster than you could say "tick." All day long, he dashed here and there, talking constantly with his chitter chatter, chitter chatter. He was never still for one minute and he was always hiding nuts where he thought no one would find them.

One day, when Chitter Chatter went to find the chestnuts which he had hidden at the foot of the cherry tree in the orchard, he discovered that they were gone.

Chitter Chatter became very much excited and he began to run around and around in circles. But when the circles made him dizzy, he sat down to rest and to think.

"Where could those chestnuts be?" thought Chitter Chatter.

He had gathered them that very morning from the chestnut tree. Then he had run lickety-clip to the orchard to hide them in what he thought was a safe place.

The more Chitter Chatter thought about the chestnuts, the more puzzled he became.

Then Chaddie Chipmunk came along.

"What is the matter, Chitter Chatter?" asked Chaddie.

"Oh, Chaddie Chipmunk,

I hid my chestnuts over there.

Now, I cannot find them anywhere."

"Go look under the birch tree," advised Chaddie. "Perhaps you hid them there by mistake."

Chitter Chatter rushed over to the birch tree, but the chestnuts were not there.

Soon Chee Chee Robin flew by. "Why are you sobbing, Chitter Chatter?" he asked.

"Oh, Chee Chee Robin,
I hid my chestnuts over there.
Now, I cannot find them anywhere.
I looked behind the birch tree,
But I did not find my chestnuts there."

"Perhaps you hid them behind the peach tree," said Chee Chee Robin.

Chitter Chatter looked, but the chestnuts were not behind the peach tree.

As Chitter Chatter continued to sob, along came Chirp Chirp Chicken. "You look very sad, Chitter Chatter," said Chirp Chirp. "May I help you?"

"Oh, Chirp Chirp Chicken,
I hid my chestnuts over there.
Now, I cannot find them anywhere.
I looked behind the birch tree and the peach tree,
But I did not find my chestnuts there."

"I have an idea," suggested Chirp Chirp. "Why don't you look in the kitchen? Perhaps someone hid them there to tease you."

So Chitter Chatter crept through a hole in the kitchen screen and looked all over the kitchen. There was not one chestnut to be found. Just as he was trying to crawl back through the screen, some children saw him.

"Oh, a squirrel," they cried. "He would make a wonderful pet. Let us catch him." So they caught Chitter Chatter and put him into a cage.

Chitter Chatter was so unhappy. He would never be able to run and play again. He was sorry that he had ever gone into the orchard to hide his chestnuts.

Suddenly, he saw the children coming toward the cage with something in their hands. "Here are some chestnuts, little squirrel. We found them at the foot of the cherry tree in the orchard. We have been waiting for you to come along, for we know how much you like chestnuts."

Chitter Chatter had his chestnuts after all. But the story does not end there.

The kind mother of the children came into the room and saw Chitter Chatter. "What a dear little squirrel!" she exclaimed. "But he shouldn't be shut up in a cage. A squirrel should have his freedom. Why do you not let him run back into the woods?"

The children let him out, of course, and away he scampered. The next day, however, Chitter Chatter was right back again begging for nuts. And why? Because the children were his friends. He never hid another nut as long as he lived, for the children took good care of him.

After the story, the children will enjoy this poem.

Little squirrel likes to frisk,
    Chitter chatter, chitter chatter,
Quinky winky, with a whisk,
    Chitter chatter, chitter chatter.
Watch him; you will see him peek,
    Chitter chatter, chitter chatter,
As he plays at hide and seek,
    Chitter chatter, chitter chatter.

JEE JEE

Jee Jee is a jumping jack,
  A jumping jack,
  A jumping jack.
Jee Jee is a jumping jack,
  He jumps about with glee.

Jee Jee pops into his box,
  Into his box,
  Into his box.
Jee Jee pops into his box,
  And says, "You can't catch me."

Since "j" is a combination of "d" and "zh," a satisfactory method of correction can be attained by having the child make a "d" several times, then "zh" several times. Then have him make "d" and "zh" in rapid succession. Refer to the instructions on making and correcting the "ch" sound, since "j" is the voiced equivalent of "ch."

JIGGETY JIG

Children: Jiggety jig, jiggety jig,
        Johnny Jumper is dancing a jig.
        Jiggety jig, jiggety jig,
        Jiggety-jiggety-jig.
1st child: He jumps up high like a jumping jack.
2nd child: He turns flip-flops around and back.
3rd child: He jumps on the table and up the stair.
4th child: He jumps six feet up in the air.
5th child: He spins around like a spinning top,
        A hundred times without a stop.
Children: Jiggety jig, jiggety jig,
        Johnny Jumper is dancing a jig.
        Jiggety jig, jiggety jig,
        Jiggety-jiggety-jig.

GINGERBREAD MAN

Solo: The old woman opened the oven to see
If the gingerbread man was done to a T.

All: Ginger and spice, ginger and spice,
A gingerbread man smells exceedingly nice.

Solo: A tiny voice cried as she opened the door,
"I want to come out and play on the floor."

All: Ginger and spice, ginger and spice,
A gingerbread man smells exceedingly nice.

Solo: The old woman called, "Come here, come here.
A gingerbread man has nothing to fear."

All: Ginger and spice, ginger and spice,
A gingerbread man smells exceedingly nice.

Solo: But he waved a good-by and he called as he ran,
"You can't catch me; I'm the gingerbread man."

All: Ginger and spice, ginger and spice,
A gingerbread man smells exceedingly nice.

After listening to the familiar fairy tale, children will enjoy the verses that also tell the story. The repetition of the words *ginger* and *gingerbread* give drill for the "j" sound used medially and initially.

Hinge Game

Teacher: Boys and girls, do you know what hinges are? If you will look around the room you will see hinges on the door. There are also hinges on the cupboard and on the lid of your desk. Point to a hinge. Hinges make the door move back and forth. Your body has hinges, too. Can you show me one of the hinges that moves like the hinges on the door? Let us play a game and move the hinges in our body. We will move only one hinge at a time. Each time that you say the word *hinge,* you are making the "Jumping Jack" sound. The sound is at the very end of the word *hinge.* Now let us find our hinges. First, your neck hinge . . . then shoulder hinge . . . elbow hinge . . . finger hinge . . . wrist hinge . . . thumb hinge . . . knee hinge . . . ankle hinge . . . toe hinge . . . Now, let all of the hinges fall gently to the floor. Let them fall very, very gently . . . slowly . . . slowly. Now, pick up your hinges carefully and stand tall again with no hinges moving at all.

One child may come to the front of the room and ask the class to move their hinges, thus getting drill on the "j" sound. This is a relaxation exercise which teaches the child to tense and relax at will.

TWO BLACKBIRDS

There were two blackbirds sitting on a hill,
    One named Jack,
    The other named Jill.
    Fly away, Jack,
    Fly away, Jill;
    Come back, Jack,
    Come back, Jill.

—MOTHER GOOSE

Have children hold up their hands with thumbs extended to represent the blackbirds. A thumb is bent down toward the palm of the hand when the bird flies away and is straightened again when the bird returns.

GINGERBREAD HOUSE

Make a paper gingerbread house which has many steps leading up to the door. On each step print a word containing the "j" sound. The children take turns climbing the steps by reading the words. If a child mispronounces a word, he starts again at the bottom of the steps. If he is unable to make a correct "j" be sure that he is given praise for trying.

jelly	jump	jug
jig	Jill	jacket
juice	Jack	Jim
John	just	jello

Show the children that the letter *g* sometimes makes the "j" sound.

bridge	cage	giant
sponge	page	orange
ginger	edge	pigeon

JOHNNY JUMPER

The entire class can take the role of Johnny Jumper, saying his little poem each time it occurs. Individual children may recite the lines of the other animals. This story can be told using paper bag or stick puppets. As children become more familiar with the stories in this book, they will use the puppets with more ease. The stories will, then, be more useful as speech improvement devices.

Johnny Jumper was a rabbit that lived on a farm with his mother and father. And since he was the only little rabbit in the family, he became very lonely at times. When this happened, Mother Rabbit would always find something that was lots of fun for Johnny Jumper to do, such as counting carrot seeds or playing "hide the lettuce leaf."

152

One day, however, when Johnny Jumper was lonely, there was no one around to think of something that would be fun. Mother Rabbit had gone shopping and Father Rabbit was out planting carrots.

"I will just have to find someone to play with me," said Johnny Jumper to himself, and away he hopped.

Soon he met a baby chick.

"My name is Johnny Jumper,
And I came by to see
If you would dance a jolly jig
Or jump awhile with me."

But the baby chick said to Johnny Jumper,
"I'm sorry, Johnny Jumper,
That's what I'd like to do,
But you are much too large,
So I cannot jump with you."

Johnny Jumper felt very sad because he was much too large to play with baby chick, but away he hopped until he met the cat.

"My name is Johnny Jumper,
And I came by to see
If you would dance a jolly jig
Or jump awhile with me."

But the cat said to Johnny Jumper,
"I'm sorry, Johnny Jumper,
That's what I'd like to do,
But I must go buy oranges,
So I cannot jump with you."

Johnny Jumper was sorry that the cat was too busy to play with him, but away he hopped until he met the dog.

"My name is Johnny Jumper,
And I came by to see
If you would dance a jolly jig
Or jump awhile with me."
But the dog said to Johnny Jumper,
"I'm sorry, Johnny Jumper,
That's what I'd like to do,
But I have to make some fudge,
So I cannot jump with you."

Johnny Jumper felt unhappy because the dog had to make fudge and could not play with him, but away he hopped until he met some squirrels.

"My name is Johnny Jumper,
And I came by to see
If you would dance a jolly jig
Or jump awhile with me."
But the squirrels said to Johnny Jumper,
"We're sorry, Johnny Jumper,
That's what we'd like to do,
But we're looking for a pigeon,
So we cannot jump with you."

Johnny Jumper was so lonesome that he lay down under a tall tree and went fast asleep. He dreamed that a little bird flew up and said, "Chirp, chirp, Johnny Jumper, wake up. Wake up. If you hurry home, you will find a wonderful surprise waiting for you."

Johnny Jumper woke up, and remembering the dream, he hurried home as fast as his rabbit legs could carry him. He peeked inside the house, and there was the surprise . . . four little rabbits playing on the floor.

154

"My name is Johnny Jumper,
And I came home to see
If you would dance a jolly jig,
Or jump awhile with me."
The four little rabbits looked at Johnny Jumper and replied,
"Yes, indeed, Johnny Jumper,
That's what we'd like to do.
We'd like to dance a jolly jig,
And jump awhile with you."
So Johnny Jumper had at last found four playmates, Jerry, and Jill, and Jack, and Joan. You may be sure that Johnny Jumper was never lonely again.

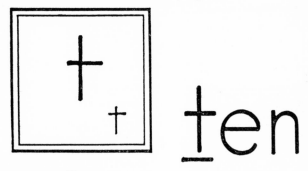

MAKING THE SOUND:

The tongue is pressed lightly against the shelf (gum ridge) behind the upper front teeth, holding the air within the mouth. The soft palate is raised to keep the air from being emitted through the nose. When the tongue is lowered quickly, the air is released suddenly and explosively as the "t" sound. The vocal cords do not vibrate and the lips and teeth are usually slightly parted. Call "t" the—

Watch sound

WORDS:

Initial	Medial	Final
ten	letter	cat
table	butter	feet
top	water	basket

BLENDS:

"tr" – train	"kt" – talked	"rt" – heart
– truck	– locked	– start
"pt" – slept	"lt" – salt	"st" – past
– hopped	– felt	– stop

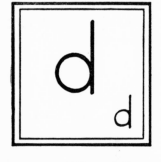 

MAKING THE SOUND:

This sound is made like the "t" sound, except that the vocal cords vibrate. The quickly lowered tongue causes the air to be released suddenly and explosively as the "d" sound.

Call "d" the—

Woodpecker sound

Typewriter sound

WORDS:

Initial	Medial	Final
dog	children	bed
dress	radio	red
doll	candy	hand

156

BLENDS:

"dr" – dress	"gd" – wagged	"vd" – lived
– drum	– begged	– moved
"bd" – grabbed	"ld" – rolled	"zd" – pleased
– robbed	– called	– raised

LITTLE WATCH

Can you be a little watch
Held closely to my ear?
    "t, t, t, t, t, t, t"
And does your tongue touch with the tip
To make the sound I hear?
    "t, t, t, t, t, t, t"

CLOCKS

"Tock, tock, tock, tock,"
Says grandfather clock in the hall.
"Tick, tock, tick, tock,"
Says the kitchen clock on the wall.
"Tick-a-tick tick, tick-a-tick tick,"
Says the alarm clock on the shelf.
"t, t, t, t, t, t, t,"
Says the watch I bought for myself.

Ask the children to feel the tips of their tongues touch the ridge behind their upper teeth as they say, "t, t, t, t, t, t, t." There is no vibration of the vocal cords in making the "watch" sound.

Tee, tee, too.
See what my pinky tongue can do.
Too, too, tee.
It touches with the tip, you see.

157

LITTLE MICE

Let us all be little mice,
Looking for a piece of cheese.
Tiptoe, tiptoe, tiptoe . . .
Watch your step, don't make a noise,
Do not cough and do not sneeze.
Tiptoe, tiptoe, tiptoe . . .
Pussy cat is sleeping near,
Sh . . . be careful, she will hear.
Tiptoe, tiptoe, tiptoe . . .

Choose three children to be the mice and one to be the pussy cat.
Let them dramatize the poem as the class says it. The teacher should
say the lines with the class doing the refrain until the children know it.

TICK, TOCK

Tick, tock, tick, tock,
Merrily sings the clock.
It's time for work,
It's time for play,
And so it sings
Through all the day.
Tick, tock, tick, tock,
Merrily sings the clock.

—Anonymous

Have the children hold up their index fingers and pretend that they
are pendulums moving back and forth to the rhythm of the poem.

MR. CLOCK

One day I said to Mr. Clock,
"All you say is 'Tock, tick, tock.' "
He said to me with a little click,
"Listen now for 'Tick, tock, tick.' "

-Anonymous

158

ORCHESTRA

Tell us what the flute is saying.

1st Group: Teedle-dee-dee, teedle-dee-dee,
Tiny notes the flute is playing,
Teedle-dee-dee, teedle-dee-dee.

Tell us what the trumpet's saying.

2nd Group: Toot toot, toot toot toot,
Loud shrill notes the trumpet's playing,
Toot toot, toot toot toot.

Tell us what the drum is saying.

3rd Group: Tumpy tum tum, tumpy tum tum,
Thumpy sounds the drum is making,
Tumpy tum tum, tumpy tum tum.

Tell us what the boy is saying.

Everyone: One, two, three; one, two, three,
While the orchestra is playing,
One, two, three; one, two, three.

TERRY TICKER

Check the children individually to be sure that each is making the voiceless sound, "t," as the "watch" sound. Encourage them to make the watch tick rapidly so that their tongues will become more flexible. After the story has been told, the teacher should walk around the room and have the children whisper the "watch" sound close to her ear.

Terry Ticker was a tiny wristwatch. He lived in a clock shop where the clocks sang a merry chorus day and night. They ticked so loudly that Terry Ticker's soft little "t, t, t, t, t, t, t" could not be heard by anyone who happened to be calling at the clock shop.

When someone made a visit to the shop, he would see the grandfather clock with its deep tock, tock, tock, or the wall clock that went tick-tock, tick-tock, or the alarm clock that ticked very fast: tick-a-tick-a-tick-a-tick, or any one of the other clocks of all sizes and shapes with their many kinds of ticks. But no one ever bothered about Terry Ticker. The sound he made, "t, t, t, t, t, t, t," was so soft that no one heard him or even stopped to look at him.

It was Christmas time and everybody was hurrying about buying presents.

One morning, a lady named Mrs. Smith rang the chimes "ting, ting, ting," and walked into the clock shop. She looked all around.

"May I help you?" asked the shopkeeper.

"Yes," said Mrs. Smith. "I want to find a Christmas gift for a little boy."

"How old is he?" asked the shopkeeper.

"Only five," replied Mrs. Smith, "but he is a very special little boy. He belongs to me. I chose him myself and that is why he is so precious."

Terry Ticker heard what was said and he ticked "t, t, t, t, t, t, t" as fast as he could to attract attention.

Then Mrs. Smith saw him. "Why, this watch is exactly what I want for my little boy," she said happily as she held Terry close to her ear. "It will make a wonderful gift."

"t, t, t, t, t, t, t," whispered Terry Ticker, "t, t, t, t, t, t, t."

"Please wrap this watch in your prettiest Christmas paper," said Mrs. Smith.

Terry Ticker kept right on ticking, "t, t, t, t, t, t, t," as the shopkeeper wrapped him. But Terry Ticker ticked with a happier sound now that he was going to belong to a very special someone.

THE RIDDLE

All day long it's "d-d-d-d-d,"
And if you're quiet as can be
You can hear the "d-d-d-d-d"
That comes from the old oak tree.
    It's "d-d-d-d-d" all morning.
    It's "d-d-d-d-d" at noon.
    It's "d-d-d-d-d" till evening comes
    To stop the busy tune.
Have you guessed yet? . . . "d-d-d-d-d" . . .
Have you guessed yet who it can be
Working like this . . . "d-d-d-d-d" . . .
In the friendly old oak tree?

As the teacher tells the poem, she should allow sufficient time for the children to come in with the "d-d-d-d-d" whenever it occurs. The children may also tap "d-d-d-d-d" with their fingers in order to accentuate the rhythm.

DIDDLE-DIDDLE-DEE

What says a duck with a yellow back?
    Diddle-diddle-dee.
A yellow duck says quack-quack-quack.
    Diddle-diddle-dee.
What says a cow when she looks at you?
    Diddle-diddle-dee.
A brown-eyed cow says moo-moo-moo.
    Diddle-diddle-dee.
And does a puppy say me-ow?
    Diddle-diddle-dee.
A puppy says bow-wow, bow-wow.
    Diddle-diddle-dee.
What says the phone when you hear it ring?
    Diddle-diddle-dee.
The phone says ting-a-ling-a-ling.
    Diddle-diddle-dee.
    Boys with toys make noise,
    And girls with curls play house.
    To end this rhyme say diddle-diddle-dee
    As quietly as a mouse.

(softer)   Diddle-diddle-dee,
(softer)   Diddle-diddle-dee,
(softer)   Diddle-diddle-dee.

CLIMBING THE LADDER

On this ladder you will see
Several words with the letter D (dee).
"d" is the sound, now don't forget,
While D (dee) is the letter of the alphabet.

dig	dust	hide
dog	dip	ride
do	red	road
desk	led	said
door	wide	fed

Draw a ladder and place a word on each rung. The children take turns climbing the ladder by reading the words. A child who mispronounces a word must start again at the base of the ladder.

FOUR LITTLE DOGS

Four little dogs met one day,
And each little dog had something to say.
The first one said, "This candy is red."
The second one said, "I moved my head."
The third one said, "I need some bread."
The fourth one said, "I'll hide in the shed."

Ask the children to listen for words that have the "d" sound and, when the poem has been said, to name as many as they can.

dog	candy	head	hide
day	red	third	shed
had	second	need	
said	moved	bread	

DONNY TYPEWRITER

Instructions for pupil participation are contained in the story itself. In addition, however, the teacher may ask the children to chorus the sound of the typewriter whenever it appears in the story.

Donny Typewriter had not been used for a long time. He wondered if anyone would ever again touch his keys. He knew that Daddy had brought home a brand new typewriter to do all his work. That was why Donny sat in the dark closet all alone collecting dust.

He could hear the "d, d, d, d, d, d, d," as Daddy typed hour after hour on the new typewriter . . . "d, d, d, d, d, d."

One day Daddy went on a trip and took the new typewriter along.

All was very quiet.

Then Donny heard, "Mummy, Mummy."

It was DeeDee, Daddy's and Mummy's little girl.

"Mummy, may I write Daddy a letter?" DeeDee asked.

"Of course, dear," replied Mummy.

"May I use the old typewriter in the closet?" asked DeeDee.

"You may, dear," said Mummy. "I will get it for you."

Mummy took Donny Typewriter from the dark closet and set him on the table.

DeeDee began to type . . . "d, d, d," . . . and then she paused.

164

"How do you spell 'Dear'?" she asked.

"D-e-a-r," answered Mummy.

"How do you spell 'Daddy'?" asked DeeDee.

"D-a-d-d-y," replied Mummy.

"d, d, d, d, d, d, d, d, d," typed Donny.

"That is the beginning of my letter," said DeeDee. "Now I will write some more." And she began to type again.

"d, d, d, d, d, d, d," clicked Donny. Then faster, "ddddddddddddd . . . ddddddddddddd."

It was a very nice letter and DeeDee was proud of it. She placed it in a pink envelope, put a stamp on it, and dropped it into the corner mailbox. Daddy received the letter the next day, and you can imagine how pleased he was.

What do you think DeeDee wrote in her letter to Daddy?

Do you think Donny Typewriter will ever be used again?

Let us pretend that our tongues are typing. Make them say "d, d, d, d, d," . . . Put your hand over your voice box and feel it move as you say the "typewriter" sound . . . "d, d, d, d, d, d, d."

Here is a poem about the "typewriter" sound . . . Listen while I read it the first time. Then you may help me say it.

> "d, d, d, d, d,"
> Was the sound I heard;
> "d, d, d, d, d,"
> As I typed a word.

165

k k <u>k</u>itty

MAKING THE SOUND:

The back of the tongue is raised and pressed against the soft palate, holding the air inside the mouth. The soft palate is raised to keep the air from being emitted through the nose. When the back of the tongue is lowered quickly, the air is released suddenly and explosively with a coughing sound. The tip of the tongue is usually on the floor of the mouth and the lips and teeth are slightly parted. The vocal cords do not vibrate.

The "k" sound has many different spellings: *k*ite, *c*at, ba*ck*, *Ch*ristmas, uni*que*, wa*lk*, li*qu*or, oc*c*ur, etc. The letters *q* and *x* are usually pronounced "kw" and "ks." Call "k" the—

Coughing sound
Crow sound

CORRECTING THE SOUND:

The "k" sound appears in infantile speech in the form of "t," i. e., *tat* for *cat, tan* for *can*. It is not an easy sound to correct if defective. The correct tongue position is very difficult to show to a child. A mirror will help, but correction should be carried on, primarily, through ear training drills.

166

WORDS:

Initial	Medial	Final
cake	picnic	black
kitten	basket	book

BLENDS:

"kl" – climb   "lk" – milk
       – clay   – silk
"kr" – crow   "rk" – fork
       – cry   – bark

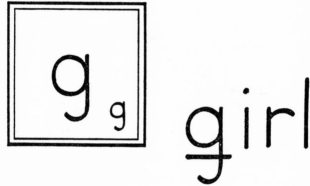

MAKING THE SOUND:

This sound is made like the "k" sound, except that the vocal cords vibrate.

Call "g" the—
Frog sound

CORRECTING THE SOUND:

Have the child place a hand on his voice box to feel the movement as he coughs. Once he can get the feel of a correct "k" sound, it will be an easy step to making the voice box "buzz" to produce a "g" sound.

WORDS:

Initial	Medial	Final
goose	sugar	frog
girl	finger	dog

BLENDS:

"gl" – glad   "gd" – tagged
     – glue   – wagged
"gr" – gray   "gz" – frogs
     – grab   – bugs
"rg" – iceberg
     – hamburger

THE COUGH SOUND

Some sounds are made a funny way;
I touch my throat and then I say:
     "k, k, k."
Just like a little cough it goes;
I cannot feel it in my nose.
     "k, k, k"
We hear the sound in "can" and "cake,"
And at the end of "talk" and "make."
     "k, k, k"
It quite surprised me when I found
That in my throat I made the sound.
     "k, k, k"
So when I listen to a word,
I try to see if I have heard:
     "k, k, k."

168

BLACK CROW

An old black crow once said to me:

All: "Caw, caw, caw,"

As he sat in an apple tree.

All: "Caw, caw, caw."

1st child: "I see some children having fun,

2nd child: I see an airplane in the sky,

3rd child: I see a lovely yellow sun,

4th child: I see an engine going by."

An old black crow sat in the tree,

All: "Caw, caw, caw,"

And those were things that he told me.

All: "Caw, caw, caw."

As they say the refrain, the sound "k" may be felt in the throat.

PIGGY WIGGY

Piggy, Wiggy, in your pen,
Oink, oink, oink,
Are you eating corn again?
Oink, oink, oink.
If you get too fat, you know,
Oink, oink, oink,
Off to market you will go,
Oink, oink, oink.

Use this poem for final "k." Make certain that children say the diphthong "oi" correctly. Emphasize the lip movement as "oink" is said.

THE WALK

Mount pictures of the animals in the story and print the sound that the animal makes below each picture. Then, as the teacher holds up a picture of an animal as it occurs in the story, the children chorus the name of the animal. When the animal sound is wanted, point to the printed animal sound and let the children respond. Individual drill may be provided by permitting one child to be an animal, making such responses as are necessary.

Other animals may be included in the story to lengthen it or to provide drill on additional sounds, such as a rooster for the "r," a goose for the "th," and a snake for the "s."

One fine morning I decided to go for a walk. So I said to my little dog *(Teacher holds up picture of a dog),* "Let's go for a walk."

He was very ready, because he jumped upon me and said, "Arf, arf." This meant, "All right, let's go," in dog talk.

We started down the road, my dog and I. When we came to a tall tree, I looked up, and there in the top of the tree was an old black crow. *(Teacher holds up picture of a crow.)*

"Good morning, Mr. Crow," I said. "We're going for a walk. Would you like to come along?"

But all Mr. Crow would say was "Caw, caw."

On we went until we came to a farm, and there by the barn was a cow. *(Teacher holds up picture of a cow.)*

"Good morning, Mrs. Cow. We're going for a walk. Would you like to come along?"

But all Mrs. Cow would say was "Moo, moo."

On we went around the barn, and there behind it in a pen was a chubby little pig. *(Teacher holds up picture of a pig.)*

"Good morning, little pig. We're going for a walk. Would you like to come along?"

But all the pig would say was "Oink, oink."

We walked across the farm until we came to a large meadow. There in the middle of the meadow was a sheep. *(Teacher holds up picture of a sheep.)*

"Good morning, Mr. Sheep. We're going for a walk. Would you like to come along?"

But all the sheep would say was "Baa, baa."

As we walked on across the meadow we came to a pond, and there swimming on it was a duck. *(Teacher holds up picture of a duck.)*

"Good morning, little duck. We're going for a walk. Would you like to come along?"

But all the duck would say was "Quack, quack."

Soon we came to a hill and started to climb, but I happened to look at the sky and saw that it was getting black and cloudy. So I said to my little dog, "It's going to rain. We had better hurry home or we will get all wet."

My little dog looked at me and said, "Arf, arf," which meant, "I agree, let's go," in dog talk.

Down the hill we went until we came to the pond. There was the duck, still swimming. *(Picture)*

"It's going to rain, little duck. You'll get all wet."

But the duck just looked at us and said, "Quack, quack."

Across the meadow we hurried until we met the sheep. *(Picture)*

"It's going to rain, Mr. Sheep. You'll get all wet."

But the sheep didn't mind. He just looked at us and said, "Baa, baa."

We hurried faster and faster and were soon at the barn. Little pig was still behind it eating corn. *(Picture)*

"It's going to rain, little pig. You'll get all wet."

But the pig didn't mind. He just looked at us and said, "Oink, oink."

Around the barn we went and, sure enough, Mrs. Cow was still there, eating hay. *(Picture)*

"It's going to rain, Mrs. Cow. You'll get all wet."

But the cow didn't mind. She just looked at us and said, "Moo, moo."

We left the farm and hurried down the road. Soon we came to the tall tree and there was the crow, still sitting high in the branches. *(Picture)*

"It's going to rain, Mr. Crow. You'll get all wet."

But the crow didn't mind. He just looked at us and said, "Caw, caw."

I was running now, and just managed to get home and inside the door when it started to pour rain. Suddenly I heard a scratch . . . scratch . . . scratch at the front door. I went to the door and opened it and what do you think it was? It was my little dog. I had forgotten to let him in with me.

"Arf, arf," he barked. This meant "Let me in, I'm getting wet" in dog talk.

So I let him in and shut the door. And that was the end of my walk, and this is the end of my story.

Barnyard Game

Children may be chosen for animals with instructions to act out the lines. The teacher reads the lines and the child moos, quacks, gobbles, etc. Be sure that the game ends with relaxation, or confusion may result.

The little red rooster crows and crows;
He flaps his wings and away he goes,
"r, r, r, r, r."

The little brown hen sits on her eggs;
She then gets up and stretches her legs,
"Cluck, cluck, cluck."

The little yellow duck as neat as a pin
Goes to the brook for a nice cool swim,
"Quack, quack, quack."

The old turkey gobbler stands on his toes;
He flaps his wings and away he goes,
"Gobble, gobble, gobble."

The little white chicken with yellow bill
Flaps his wings and flies over the hill,
"Cheep, cheep, cheep."

The old gray goose that everyone knows
Flaps his wings and away he goes,
"th ... th ... th ..."

173

The jersey cow that is eating hay
Switches her tail and runs away,
  "Moo, moo, moo."

The little brown colt all frisky and gay
Kicks his heels and gallops away,
  "Ee . . . ee . . . ee . . ."

The little green snake that is lying near
Says, "I'll wiggle away, for I shouldn't be here.
  "s . . . s . . . s . . ."

The old billy goat, when he wants to eat,
Shakes his horns and stamps his feet,
  "Maa, maa, maa."

The little gray donkey, who likes to bray,
Shakes his head and gallops away,
  "Ee-aw, ee-aw, ee-aw."

The guinea hen sits up in a tree,
And scolds everybody that she can see,
  "Put-rack, put-rack, put-rack."

The woolly sheep comes out of his pen;
He looks around and goes back again,
  "Baa, baa, baa."

The little black pig with a curly tail
Stops eating his dinner out of the pail,
  "Oink, oink, oink."

And then Mister Sun begins to shine,
And everyone has a wonderful time.
(*All moo, bray, cluck, etc., at once. One
child may hold up a picture of the sun.*)

Then the yellow moon comes out of the west,
And they all go home to sleep and rest.
(*Child may hold up picture of a moon as the
children tiptoe to their seats.*)

Teacher: Rest, rest, rest in your little nests.
Let us see who can do it the best.
You can be still, still, still
If you only will.

Words having the "k" sound:			
crows	chicken	snake	oink
cluck	kicks	shakes	black
cow	colt	donkey	comes
duck	frisky	put-rack	turkey
curly			

Words having the "g" sound			
goes	gobble	goose	gallops
wiggle	eggs	gray	gay
green	goat	guinea	pig

GO! GO! GO!

All:
We went to see the streamline train
Racing down the track.
"Go, silver streamline train,
But please hurry back."

1st child: "Go," said Mary, "Go, go, go."
2nd child: "Go," said John, "Go, go, go."
3rd child: "Go," said Jane, "Go, go, go."

All:
We went to see the fire truck,
Its siren roaring loud.
"Go, red fire engine,
But watch out for the crowd."

4th child: "Go," said David, "Go, go, go."
5th child: "Go," said Susan, "Go, go, go."
6th child: "Go," said Jerry, "Go, go, go."

All:
We went to see the airplanes
Soaring through the blue.
"Go, you flying airplanes.
We would like to be with you."

7th child: "Go," said Sally, "Go, go, go."
8th child: "Go," said Jimmy, "Go, go, go."
9th child: "Go," said Betty, "Go, go, go."

All:
"Go, streamliner, go, go, go;
Go, fire engine, go, go, go;
Go, flying airplane, go, go, go."

Each child should substitute his own name as he says his line. Use mounted pictures as visual aids for the poem.

WATER BOTTLE

Have a child tip a small bottle and pretend to be pouring water as he says: "g, g, g," "gug, gug, gug," or "gurgle, gurgle, gurgle" to imitate the water. Show him that the sound is felt in the voice box. Apply it in a word as soon as possible.

> I hold my water bottle so,
> Then you can hear the water go:
> "g, g, g, g, g, g."
> I always hold my bottle up
> As water goes into my cup.
> "g, g, g, g, g, g,"
> I do not spill a single drop,
> For when my cup is full, I stop.
> "g, g, g, g, g, g."

NONSENSE VERSES

— 1 —

A good, good girl saw a gray, gray goose
　　Chased by a big, big dog.
The gray, gray goose and the big, big dog
　　Jumped to a green, green log.
The good, good girl grabbed the big, big dog
　　And said, "Now go and dig."
So the big, big dog left the gray, gray goose
　　And went to dig with the pig.

Who has seen:
    A big pig dig
    Or a frog on a log in a bog?
Who has seen:
    A leg beg an egg
    Or a dog get lost in a fog?

THE FROGS

Let the children make the sounds of the Frog Family after the teacher has said the desired word or sound. It must be remembered that repetition has no value unless the teacher takes steps to see that each child is repeating the correct sounds or words. Otherwise, it is the defective speech pattern which benefits from the drill and no progress is being made.

A family of frogs lived in a bog, which is a watery wet place. Everything was watery wet . . . the grass, the trees, the lily pads, and, of course, the pond which was the watery wettest of all.

There was Grandfather Frog who croaked, "Gunk, gunk, gunk," in a loud voice, and Grandmother Frog who croaked, "Glug, glug, glug," in a lesser loud voice.

Then there was Father Frog who croaked, "Gub, gub, gub," in a rather soft voice, and Mother Frog who croaked, "Gum, gum, gum," in a sort of hum.

Baby Frog said, "g, g, g," in the softest voice of all. When he made that sound, you could see his throat move just a wee bit.

And when the Frog Family croaked all at the same time they made quite a chorus indeed.

The Frog Family were all as green as green. They had tongues that were redder than red. Often their tongues popped out of their mouths when they wanted to catch bugs. Very often they caught the bugs, too.

It would be fun to play games about the frogs. Let us make our tongues help us play this game:

> Froggie's tongue looks out and in,
> Froggie's tongue looks down to chin,
> Froggie's tongue looks out and up,
> Froggie's tongue looks like a cup.

Hold up one hand and pretend that the fingers are frogs. Listen and watch the first time I say this poem. Then we will say it together.

One hand is held up with fingers extended. The other hand is used to grasp the extended fingers one at a time as each line is said.

> This green frog says, "Gunk, gunk, gunk."
> This green frog says, "Glug, glug, glug."
> This green frog says, "Gub, gub, gub."
> This green frog says, "Gum, gum, gum."
> And Baby Frog says, "g, g, g, g, g, g,"
> Because he is such a little one.

Now let us pretend that we are all frogs sitting on a lily pad in the middle of a blue pond. Close your eyes and see the lily pad . . . It is green, and big, and round . . . Your feet are tucked under you . . . Your hands are folded . . . The sun is warm on your back . . . The bees hum a drowsy song . . . The wind makes the lily pad rock so gently . . . so gently . . . All the frogs sit very still . . . sleepy . . . sleepy still.

Use this last "pretend" game for relaxation. It can be used at other times as well as with this particular story.

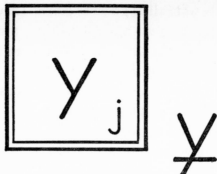

y **you**

Making the Sound:

The tongue is pressed lightly against the sides of the teeth in position for the sound of "ee." The lips are parted and drawn back slightly. The soft palate is raised and the vocal cords are vibrated. The lips and tongue glide immediately into position for the vowel sound which follows.

Children may be aided in making the sound correctly by having them make the sound of "ee" followed by the sound of "uh," . . . "ee-uh" . . . "ee-uh." As the two sounds are repeated more rapidly they blend into the sound of "y."

The "y" sound is explained here as a consonant sound (note the words in the list below). The vowel qualities of the letter *y*, as used in spelling, i. e., *pony, my,* and *softly,* are not discussed in this book.

Call "y" the—

Puppy sound

Words:

Initial	Medial
yellow	canyon
yarn	onion
yawn	vineyard

180

MY PUPPY

There's a puppy lives at my house,
Children: Yip, yip, yip, yip, yip.
And how he loves to chase a mouse,
Children: Yip, yip, yip, yip, yip.
His ears are long, his nose is black,
Children: Yip, yip, yip, yip, yip.
He wags in front, he wags in back,
Children: Yip, yip, yip, yip, yip.
When we go walking in the park,
Children: Yip, yip, yip, yip, yip.
He wants to stay till it is dark,
Children: Yip, yip, yip, yip, yip.
But every day, my little pup,
Children: Yip, yip, yip, yip, yip.
Will grow and grow, 'till he grows up,
Children: Yip, yip, yip, yip, yip.

YELLOW, YELLOW

Yellow, yellow sunshine
On a green hill;
Yellow, yellow flowers
Standing very still;
Yellow, yellow leaves
Falling from the tree;
Yellow, yellow duckling,
What do you see?

Use pictures to help tell the story. They will cue the children as to
which line follows which and when to chorus their refrains. Choose a
child to be the yellow, yellow duckling and let him tell the class what
he might see in just such a setting as is described in the poem.

NEW YEAR

New year, new year,
What do you bring?
I bring a happy song
For you to sing.
New year, new year,
What do you say?
Wear a happy smile
To greet each day.

This poem can be used around the first of a new year as an opening for a discussion of what the children expect during the coming year.

YES, YES, YES

Mister Spider, what are you spinning?
1st child: Can't you guess?
Are you spinning webs of silver?
1st child: Yes, yes, yes.
Little Bear, why are you crying?
2nd child: Can't you guess?
Did someone eat your breakfast porridge?
2nd child: Yes, yes, yes.
Mother Hubbard, where are you going?
3rd child: Can't you guess?
To get a bone for your poor doggie?
3rd child: Yes, yes, yes.
Tommy Tucker, why are you singing?
4th child: Can't you guess?
Are you singing for your supper?
4th child: Yes, yes, yes.

Have each child hold up a picture to illustrate his action as the questions are asked. Additional actions may be added as desired.

IS THE SKY YELLOW?

Is the sky yellow, yellow as can be?
No, the sky is blue, as you can plainly see.

Is the grass yellow, yellow as can be?
No, the grass is green, as you can plainly see.

Is a fire engine yellow, yellow as can be?
No, a fire engine's red, as you can plainly see.

Is the snow yellow, yellow as can be?
No, the snow is white, as you can plainly see.

Then tell me what is yellow, yellow as can be.
The shining sun is yellow, as you can plainly see.

A baby duck is yellow, yellow as can be.
A daffodil is yellow, as you can plainly see.

Teacher: Can you think of other things that are yellow?

If possible, have pictures which the children may hold up when the question is asked. Let one child ask the question, while the class gives the response.

Drill for the Consonant "y"

Use farm animal cutouts for this game. The child puts each animal into an enclosure saying: "I put the horse in the barnyard," "I put the cow in the barnyard." Drill is thus obtained for the medial "y" sound in the word *barnyard.*

SLEEPY PUPPY

Most children have called a dog, at some time or other, with the sound of "y, y, y, y." They can be asked to tell how they would call a puppy and whether or not they have ever called their dogs as the people in the story will call the puppy. Explain to the children how they are to help call the puppy in the story. Hold up a picture of a sleeping puppy when they are to chorus their "y, y, y, y, puppy, y, y, y, y."

Once there was a small puppy who would never come when he was called. He would just lie and snooze hour after hour. Whenever Bobby Boy wanted to play with him, he would snore loudly, "Z-Z-Z-."

Bobby Boy would say, "Here, puppy; here, puppy," but the puppy would open one sleepy eye and then go back to sleep.

Mother tried to coax the puppy by saying, "Nice puppy, here is your dinner. Come and eat it while it is fresh and tastes good."

But the puppy would snore loudly, "Z-Z-Z-." He just did not seem to care.

One day Daddy came home and saw the sleepy puppy lying on a rug with his paws stretched out. Bobby Boy said to Daddy, "Can you wake up my puppy, Daddy? All he wants to do is sleep and sleep and sleep. I want to play with him."

"I'll see what I can do," said Daddy. So he said, "Come, puppy, wake up."

The puppy only wiggled one ear and kept right on sleeping.

Then Daddy said, "y, y, y, y, puppy, y, y, y, y."

The puppy opened his eyes, perked up his ears, and sat up.

"y, y, y, y, puppy, y, y, y, y," called Daddy again. Sleepy puppy came running to Daddy, wagging his tail so hard that Bobby Boy thought it would fall off.

"Well," said Daddy. "He likes that sound."

Bobby Boy liked the sound, too, because every time he called now, "y, y, y, y, puppy, y, y, y, y," the puppy would come on the run.

Can you make the sound Bobby Boy and his Daddy made? Listen for the sound of "y, y, y, y," as I say: yellow . . . yes . . . you . . . yum yum . . . yet . . . young. We hear it at the beginning of each word. Listen for it now in the middle of these words: amuse . . . million . . . onion.

"y, y, y, y, y," I call to puppy
    when I want to play.
"y, y, y, y, y." He jumps and
    frisks about so gay.
"Yip, yip, yip, yip, yip," he says,
"I like you, can't you see?"
"Yip, yip, yip, yip, yip," he says,
"I hope that you like me."

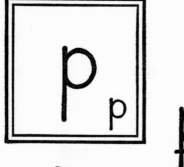

MAKING THE SOUND:

The lips are shut tightly holding the air inside the mouth. The soft palate is raised to keep the air from being emitted through the nose. When the lips are opened quickly, the air is released suddenly and explosively as the "p" sound. The teeth are usually slightly parted. There is no vibration of the vocal cords.

Call "p" the—

Tug boat sound

CORRECTING THE SOUND:

This is an easily imitated sound because it is made primarily with the lips. To demonstrate the explosive quality of the sound, have a child hold up a small bit of paper close to his mouth and say "p." The paper will move if the sound is correctly made. In cleft palate or post-polio speech, it may be necessary to close the lips more firmly than usual and exaggerate the position. If a child is prone to puff out the cheeks, ask him to hold a finger against the side of his face to see that the cheeks are not in this exaggerated position.

WORDS:

Initial	Medial	Final
pen	apple	ship
pig	paper	rope
purple	puppy	cup

BLENDS:

"pl" – please	"lp" – help
– plum	– scalp
"pr" – prince	"rp" – sharp
– pray	– carpenter

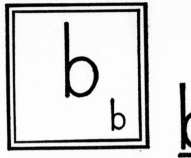

Making the Sound:

This sound is made like the "p" sound, except that the vocal cords vibrate and the lips are not pressed quite so tightly together. Like "p," it is an easily imitated sound. Call "b" the—

Brook sound

Words:

Initial	*Medial*	*Final*
book	baby	bathtub
bird	rabbit	cub

Blends:

"bl" – blue	"br" – branch	"rb" – barber
– blow	– bread	– garbage

TUG BOAT

All together, girls and boys,
Make a little puffing noise:
    "p, p, p, p, p, p, p."
Put your lips together, so;
Let your little tug boat go
    "p, p, p, p, p, p, p."
Take it all around the lake,
As the engine sound you make:
    "p, p, p, p, p, p, p."

187

PUMP, PUMP, PUMP

Pump, pump, pump, pump,
　　Water from the spout;
　　　　Plish, plosh, plish, plosh,
　　　　　　Water gushes out.
Pour, pour, pour, pour,
　　Fill the doggie's pan;
　　　　Pump, pump, pump, pump,
　　　　　　Quickly as you can.

Children go through motions indicative of pouring and pumping.

THE LITTLE BIRD

Once I saw a little bird
　　Go hop, hop, hop.
I said, "Little birdie,
　　Will you stop, stop, stop?"
He looked me up and down
　　With a peep, peep, peep.
And across the grass he went
　　With a leap, leap, leap.
　　　　　　　　—Adapted

Use flash cards with the words *hop, leap, stop,* and *peep.*

POPCORN MAN

Teacher: Pretend that you are a popcorn man selling popcorn. The class will pop the corn and you may take turns at selling it for five cents a bag.

Child: Good day, Mister Popcorn Man.

Man: Good day. Would you like to buy some popcorn?

Child: If you please.

Man: I will pop some for you. Listen to the popcorn machine.

Class: Pop, pop, pop, pop, pop, pop, pop, pop, pop, pop, pop, pop, pop, stop.

Child: Thank you, Mr. Popcorn Man.

Man: That will be five cents, please.

Child: One, two, three, four, five.

Man: Thank you.

This simple dramatization will provide drill on the "p" sound. Tell the class that they may all be the popcorn machine. Be sure that the final "p" sound at the end of *pop* is heard.

BROOK TALK

Little brook, tell me a secret;
Please talk to me, if you will.
Whisper it softly into my ear;
I will listen still ... so still.
"b, b, b, b, b, b, b"
If I press both my lips together,
I am sure I can talk like you,
For I need your sound, if I am to say,
"Betty and Bob and Boy Blue."
"b, b, b, b, b, b, b"

Check the children to see if they are closing their lips and making "b" in a short, quick manner. There may be a tendency for the children to say *buh.* "b" by itself has no vowel sound with it and is more likely to be correctly pronounced if the refrain is made in a staccato.

189

BROWN BIRDIE

Little brown birdie is bobbing his head,
  Bobbety, bobbety, bob,
Looking for something behind the shed,
  Bobbety, bobbety, bob.
I am going to watch him; perhaps I shall learn,
  Bobbety, bobbety, bob,
If his dinner will be a fat bug or a worm,
  Bobbety, bobbety, bob.

BAA, BAA, BLACK SHEEP

Baa, baa, black sheep,
Have you any wool?
Yes sir, yes sir, three bags full;
One bag for Bobby,
And one bag for Bill,
And one bag for Betty who lives on the hill.

Baa, baa, black sheep,
Have you gone astray?
Yes sir, yes sir, a very long way.
I'm most fond of Bobby,
Of Betty and of Bill,
But I would rather live with you,
So take me, if you will.

This adaptation from Mother Goose has repetition with which the child is already familiar and can easily be followed in the second reading. On the third reading, the child may raise the index finger when he hears a word with the "b" sound.

BABY'S BONNET

A bonnet, a bonnet,
A little blue bonnet,
A bonnet for baby to wear.
A bonnet, a bonnet,
With blue ribbons on it
For baby with curly brown hair.

Substitute names of children in the class and let each choose the color of bonnet to be worn. The name of the child should be used in place of the word *baby*.

WHITE BUNNY

All: Nibble, nibble, nib,
Goes white Easter Bunny;
Nibble, nibble, nib.

1st Solo: He tweaks his nose
At a brier bush rose.

2nd Solo: His tail is a puff
Made of fluff like a muff.

All: Nibble, nibble, nib,
Goes white Easter Bunny;
Nibble, nibble, nib.

3rd Solo: He gives me a wink
Of an eye so pink;

4th Solo: Then his ears flip flop,
And he's gone . . . hip hop.

All: Nibble, nibble, nib,
Goes white Easter Bunny;
Nibble, nibble, nib.

Let the class make paper bag puppets to help tell this Easter poem. See the section on "Devices to Use with This Book" for instructions. White paper bags will be far more effective than the usual brown ones.

BLACK BEETLE

Big black beetle said one day,
"Little bug, you're in my way.
Little bug, don't bother me;
I'm a big bug, don't you see?"
Little bug said, "I can do
Quite as many things as you."

—*Anonymous*

GOLDFISH

"Gub, gub, gub,"
Says my goldfish in the pool,
"Gub, gub, gub."
His fins go in and out;
He's hungry, I've no doubt.
I'll feed him now,
Before I go to school.
"Gub, gub, gub."

The "b" sound on the end of *gub* should be pronounced with emphasis in order to give the children the feeling of the lips moving together.

BUBBLE BATH

Bubble bath, bubble bath,
In a white tub.
Hear the little bubbles go
Bub, bub, bub.

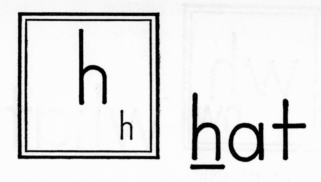

MAKING THE SOUND:

The vocal cords are partially closed, but not enough to make them vibrate. The lips, tongue, and teeth are in position for the speech sound which immediately follows the "h." The soft palate is raised. The breath makes a slight noise as it is pushed through the throat. This sound is a continuant; that is, it can be made continuously without being interrupted or forced out in an explosive manner as are the sounds of "p," "b," "t," and "d."

Call "h" the—

Panting puppy sound
Huffing sound

WORDS:

Initial	*Medial*
hand	grasshopper
horse	behind
hat	overhead

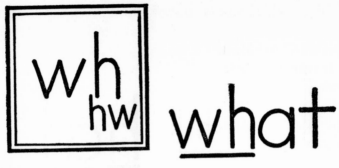

Making the Sound:

The lips are rounded as for "oo." The back of the tongue is elevated toward the soft palate. As the breath is blown out in a steady stream, the tongue, teeth, and lips move quickly and smoothly from the initial position, as in "oo," to the position for the following sound. The soft palate is raised and the vocal cords do not vibrate.

"wh" is one of the consonant sounds most frequently misarticulated. "w" is the usual substitution. Observation reveals that a major phonetic change in American speech is probably under way, since the "w" substitution is being heard and accepted more and more often.

Call "wh" the—

Pinwheel sound
Blowing sound

Correcting the Sound:

In making "wh," the blowing out of the breath precedes the actual sound itself. Children may observe this by pretending that their fingers are candles. As they blow out the candles, they first feel their breath against the fingers. Continuing to blow, they let their jaws drop down and form the "wh" part of the sound. The teacher should demonstrate this technique first.

A pinwheel will help show the correct and incorrect production of the "wh" sound. Have each child construct a pinwheel to hold before his face as he makes a "wh" into it. If correctly made, the "wh" sound will make the pinwheel spin. If the "wh" is incorrectly made, the pinwheel will not move. See the section on "Devices to Use with This Book" for instructions on making a pinwheel.

WORDS:

Initial	*Medial*
what	somewhat
where	everywhere
why	awhile

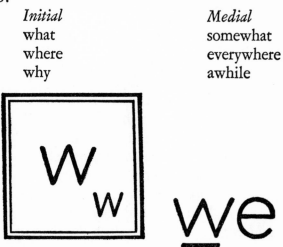

MAKING THE SOUND:

This sound is made like the "wh" sound, except that the vocal cords vibrate and the breath is not blown out forcibly as for the "wh."

Children may be aided in making this sound correctly by having them make the sound of "oo" followed by the sound of "uh," . . . "oo-uh," . . . "oo-uh." As the two sounds are repeated more rapidly, they blend into the sound of "w."

Call "w" the—

Wolf sound

WORDS:

Initial	*Medial*
water	sandwich
walk	awake
wash	between

BLENDS:

"kw" – queen   "tw" – twelve   "sw" – sweater
— quack   — twenty   — swing

COCKER SPANIEL

Tired little cocker spaniel,
Stop your play.
No more chasing after kitty:
That's enough today.
Children: "h, h, h, h, h, h, h"
Tired little cocker spaniel,
Do not run.
Close your eyes; no more excitement;
You have had your fun.
Children: "h, h, h, h, h, h, h"

This poem illustrates "h" as a breath sound. Have the children take a deep breath and imitate the panting puppy. The second panting refrain should be done very quietly. For building breath control, ask children to take a big breath and see how many panting sounds they can make on one expiration.

HAVE YOU SEEN?

Have you seen a puppy run?
Have you seen a puppy play?
Have you seen a puppy rest?
Have you heard a puppy say,
    "h, h, h, h, h, h, h, h"?

196

JOLLY SANTA

"Ho, ho, ho," laughs jolly Santa,
"Ha, ha, ha, ho, ho, ho;
My sleigh is packed, my reindeer ready.
Ho, ho, ho, off I go."

HEE-HAW

1st child: When I was visiting the farm,
I saw a donkey in the barn.
All: "Hee-haw, hee-haw,
Hee-haw, hee-haw."
2nd child: Legs so short and ears so long;
I listened to his noisy song:
All: "Hee-haw, hee-haw,
Hee-haw, hee-haw."

HUFF! PUFF!

"I'll huff and I'll puff,"
The old wolf cried,
"And I'll blow your little house in."
"Ho, ho," said the piggy,
"Ha, ha," said he,
"Not by the hair of my chinny-chin-chin."

Tell the story of "The Three Little Pigs" and dramatize it.

LAUGH WITH ME

Solo: Christmas time is coming soon, can't you see?
So, come everybody, laugh with me . . .

Children: Ha, ha,
Ho, ho,
He, he, he;
Ha, ha, ho, ho, he, he, he;

Solo: Think of all the gifts beneath the Christmas
tree.
So, come everybody, laugh with me . . .

Children: Ha, ha,
Ho, ho,
He, he, he;
Ha, ha, ho, ho, he, he, he.

Solo: Old Mister Santa Claus will visit you and me.
So, come everybody, laugh with me . . .

Children: Ha, ha,
Ho, ho,
He, he, he;
Ha, ha, ho, ho, he, he, he.

This exercise is used for breath control and vowel drill. Have the children place their hands on their diaphragms in order to feel the rapid muscular movements as they say the refrain.

OH . . . EE . . . AH

My lips are very round when I say "OH,"
My lips are in a smile when I say "EE,"
My jaw drops far, far down when I say "AH."

OH . . . EE . . . AH
Ho . . . he . . . ha

EE . . . AH . . . OH
He . . . ha . . . ho

AH . . . OH . . . EE
Ha . . . ho . . . he

Many children have poor enunciation because they do not use their lips and jaws properly. This exercise will help overcome this problem.

WISE OLD OWL

Teacher: A wise old owl who lives in a tree
Comes out at night when he can see.
All: "Hoooo . . .
Hoo – hoo – hoo
Hoooo . . ."
Teacher: He flies about so quietly
To where a little mouse might be.
All: "Hoooo . . .
Hoo – hoo – hoo
Hoooo . . ."
Teacher: Then back he flies to sleep all day.
Just listen; you will hear him say:
All: "Hoooo . . .
Hoo – hoo – hoo
Hoooo . . ."

199

MISTER OWL

When the twinkling stars come out,
Mister Owl will hoot and shout,
    Hoo, hoo, hoo,
    Hoo, hoo, hoo.
Our day time is sunny bright;
That is Mister Hoot Owl's night.
    Hoo, hoo, hoo,
    Hoo, hoo, hoo.

THE PIN WHEEL SOUND

Blow the pin wheel round and round,
    "wh, wh, wh."
Voice is quiet, not a sound,
    "wh, wh, wh."
"wh" in where, "w" in wear,
"wh" in which, "w" in witch.
Feel the difference as you blow,
    "wh, wh, wh."
Lips are rounded as you go,
    "wh, wh, wh."

Have the children make pinwheels to use in saying this poem. See the section on "Devices to Use with This Book" for instructions.

TEN LITTLE CANDLES

Ten little candles on a chocolate cake;
  "wh! wh!" Now there are eight.
Eight little candles on a candlestick;
  "wh! wh!" Now there are six.
Six little candles, and not one more;
  "wh! wh!" Now there are four.
Four little candles, red, white, and blue;
  "wh! wh!" Now there are two.
Two little candles standing in the sun;
  "wh! wh!" Now there is none.

Hold up both hands with fingers extended. Pretend the fingers are candles and that you are blowing them out. Bend a finger into the palm of the hand with each "wh."

BIRTHDAY CANDLES

Solo: Today I have a birthday.
  I'm six years old you see.
  And here I have a birthday cake
  Which you may share with me.
  First we count the candles,
  Count them, every one.
All: One ... two ... three ... four ... five ... six.
Solo: The counting now is done.
  Let's snuff out the candles,
  Out each flame will go ...
All: "wh ... wh ... wh ... wh ... wh ... wh ..."
  As one by one we blow.

A different number may be substituted in line 2 to match the age of any child having a birthday. A cardboard cake with removable candles and paper flames will add to the fun as the children blow out each candle with a "wh." See the section on "Devices to Use with This Book."

WHIPPETY WHOPPETY WHEE

There was an old owl that sat in a tree,
And the way that he acted was funny to see.

All: WHIPPETY WHOPPETY WHEE
His big yellow eyes, as round as a wheel,
Shone like the lights of an automobile.

All: WHIPPETY WHOPPETY WHEE
Now, most owls are white, so it has been said,
But that isn't true in the books I have read.

All: WHIPPETY WHOPPETY WHEE
Oh, well, does it matter what color he is,
The way that he flies or in what tree he lives?

All: WHIPPETY WHOPPETY WHEE
The question today to be answered by you
Is: WHO, WHO? WHO? WHO?

All: WHIPPETY WHOPPETY WHEE

It has been observed that many children and adults do not make a differentiation between the voiceless "wh" sound and the voiced "w" sound, pronouncing *what* as *watt,* and *white* as *wite.* This nonsense jingle provides an opportunity to emphasize the "pinwheel" sound in words in which it should be heard, "WHIPPETY WHOPPETY WHEE."

202

THE GRAY WOLF

Teacher: Once I saw a gray wolf in the zoo. He looked at me and gruffed, "w, w, w, w, w, w." Of course, that is the first sound in his name, and that is the sound we call the "wolf" sound. When I make it, my lips first say "oo"; then they say "uh." If I say "oo-uh" very quickly, it sounds like this ... "oo-uh" ... "oo-uh" ... "w" ... "w" ... "w." Listen for it at the beginning of these words ... water ... watch ... well ... wolf ... Listen for it while I read this poem. Then you may pretend that you are wolves and help me say the poem again.

> In the zoo I sometimes see
> "w, w, w,"
> An old gray wolf who talks to me,
> "w, w, w."
> But when he makes this gruffy sound,
> Wuff, wuff, wuff,
> I do not like to be around,
> Wuff, wuff, wuff.

"w" is a sound that looks like "wh" on the lips, but it has vocal cord vibration while "wh" is voiceless. Have the children practice these words to hear and feel the difference:

wear — where	witch — which
watt — what	y — why
we'll — wheel	wile — while
wail — whale	wen — when

203

THE PICNIC

Let the children take the parts of each animal or fowl, asking the questions: "Where are you going?" "Which way will you go?" "What shall I bring?"

Tell the children to blow on their fingers when they say the words *where, which,* and *what,* so that they will know whether they are saying the sound correctly. If the "wh" sound is correctly made, the child should be able to feel a strong breath blow against the fingers.

Additional animals may be included in the story to increase class participation. The magic flannel board may be effectively used as a visual aid in telling the story. See the section on "Devices to Use with This Book" for instructions.

One fine spring day I decided to go on a picnic. I went to the kitchen to see what I could find for my lunch. I put a sandwich, an apple, some potato chips, and a piece of pie in a basket and started off. I hadn't gone far when I met the cat.

"Meow, meow, where are you going?"

"I'm going on a picnic."

"Which way will you go?"

"Down by the meadow where the brook runs by. Why don't you come with me?"

"What shall I bring? I know, I'll bring . . ." *(Let the child playing the part of the cat select something to take on the picnic.)*

The cat and I walked on until we met the dog.

"Arf, arf, where are you going?"

"We're going on a picnic."

"Which way will you go?"

"Down by the meadow where the brook runs by. Why don't you come with us?"

"What shall I bring? I know, I'll bring . . ." *(Let the*

child playing the part of the dog select something to take on the picnic.)

The cat and the dog and I walked on until we met the rooster.

" 'r-r-r-r-r,' where are you going?"

"We're going on a picnic."

"Which way will you go?"

"Down by the meadow where the brook runs by. Why don't you come with us?"

"What shall I bring? I know, I'll bring . . ." *(Let the child playing the part of the rooster select something to take on the picnic.)*

The cat and the dog and the rooster and I walked on until we met a baby bear.

" 'Gr-r-r-r,' where are you going?"

"We're going on a picnic."

"Which way will you go?"

"Down by the meadow where the brook runs by. Why don't you come with us?"

"What shall I bring? I know, I'll bring . . ."

When baby bear told us what he would bring, we all turned right around and went back home as fast as we could and had our picnic on the front lawn.

Can you guess what baby bear wanted to bring along with him that made us go back home?

(Let the children guess until someone guesses that the baby bear wanted to bring his daddy and mommy.)

That's right. And when baby bear told us that he would bring his daddy and mommy, we were afraid that we would end up by being a picnic for the bears. That is why we had our picnic on the front lawn.

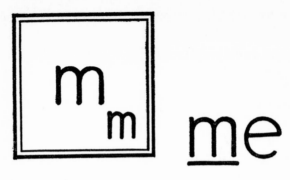

Making the Sound:

This sound is made like the "p" sound in that the lips are pressed together lightly to prevent the air from escaping through the mouth. However, the soft palate is lowered to permit the air to pass out through the nose with a humming sound. The vocal cords vibrate. The tongue is relaxed in a flat position in the mouth and the teeth are slightly parted.

Call "m" the—

Top sound

Mother Mosquito sound (See the story "How Millie Mosquito Learned to Hum.")

Correcting the Sound:

Many voices lack resonance because the breath stream is not being properly directed through the nose. In such cases, humming exercises will help improve the quality of the voice. Humming a familiar tune with the "m" sound is one of the easiest and most adaptable of such exercises. The child should be able to feel the vibrations of the "m" sound in the cheeks, the nose, the forehead, and the neck.

The nasal quality of this sound may be demonstrated by saying "m" and then pinching the nostrils together. The sound is stopped abruptly.

WORDS:

Initial	*Medial*	*Final*
mouse	Christmas	ice cream
milk	lemon	gum
monkey	hammer	comb

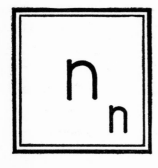 nose

MAKING THE SOUND:

This sound is made like the "t" sound in that the tip of the tongue lightly touches the little shelf (gum ridge) behind the upper teeth. As in the "m" sound, the soft palate is lowered and the air passes out through the nose to produce a nasal sound. The vocal cords vibrate and the lips and teeth are usually parted.

Call "n" the—

Sewing machine sound

Baby Mosquito sound (See the story "How Millie Mosquito Learned to Hum.")

CORRECTING THE SOUND:

The children should exaggerate the mouth opening, at first, in practicing the "n" sound so that the teacher may check to see that they are using their tongues correctly. The tongue is sometimes narrowed and sometimes pointed, depending upon the vowel following the *n*. Compare "n" to "t" and "d" and show the children that all three are made with the tongue tip in the same position. If the "n" sounds like "d," it may be an indication of an adenoidal condition or some other kind of blockage of the nasal passages.

The nasal quality of this sound may be demonstrated by saying "n" and then pinching the nostrils together. The sound is stopped abruptly.

WORDS:

Initial	Medial	Final
nose	penny	brown
knee	window	one
nine	raining	train

MAKING THE SOUND:

This sound is made similar to the "k" sound in that the rear portion of the tongue is raised to contact the soft palate. In the "ng" sound, however, the soft palate is lowered to permit the air to pass out through the nose to produce a nasal sound. The vocal cords vibrate throughout. The lips and the teeth are slightly parted and the tip of the tongue is usually on the floor of the mouth.

The "ng" sound is one of those most frequently defective. "n" is the usual substitution, i. e., *talkin'* and *singin'* for *talking* and *singing*.

Call "ng" the—

Humming sound

Daddy Mosquito sound (See the story "How Millie Mosquito Learned to Hum.")

CORRECTING THE SOUND:

Use mirrors to help the children note the difference between "ng" and "m," and "ng" and "n." A wide open mouth will let a child check his tongue position. The width of the mouth opening may be decreased after the child has learned how to produce the sound.

It is common in certain localities of the country and in certain foreign dialects to add a *hard g* sound to the end of *ing* words, i. e., *sing(g)* and *thinking(g)*. Ear training is essential in such instances.

The nasal quality of this sound may be demonstrated by saying "ng" and then pinching the nostrils together. The sound is stopped abruptly.

WORDS:

Medial	*Final*
monkey	ring
finger	morning
blanket	spring

A TOP

A top is such a lot of fun;
   "m ... m ... m ..."
Wind it up and it will run.
   "m ... m ... m ..."
Twirly, twirly, twirly, twirl,
   "m ... m ... m ..."
Whirly, whirly, whirly, whirl.
   "m ... m ... m ..."
Faster, faster, faster ... slow ...
   "m ... m ... m ..."
Stop awhile; then let it go,
   "m ... m ... m ..."

The sound "m" is one of the nasals that help to give resonance to the voice. As children say the refrain, the "m" should be made softly. It is important to feel the sound in the nose. It will demonstrate to the children that the nose is one of the important speech helpers. One child may take a turn at being a top. He takes a deep breath and sees how long he can hum before running down.

EENY, MEENY, MINY, MOE

A child is chosen to be the leader. He says, "Eeny, meeny, miney, moe," pointing to another child as he does so. The child indicated gives a word that has the "m" sound in it. He then becomes the leader and the game continues as before.

For reading readiness, a list of words containing the "m" sound in the initial, medial, and final positions may be placed on a chart with corresponding pictures.

THREE LITTLE KITTENS

Solo: Three little kittens put on their mittens
               To eat their Christmas pie.

Children: Meow, meow, meow, meow,
               To eat their Christmas pie.

Solo: Three little kittens they lost their mittens
               And they began to cry.

Children: Meow, meow, meow, meow,
               And they began to cry.

Solo: "You naughty kittens, go find those mittens,
               Or you shall have no pie."

Children: Meow, meow, meow, meow,
               "Or you shall have no pie."

Solo: The three little kittens they found their mittens.
               "Now we can have some pie."

Children: Meow, meow, meow, meow,
               "Now we can have some pie."

—Anonymous

MELINDA LIKES TO MOO

Melinda is a brown-eyed cow that says
    "Moo-moo, moo-moo,"
Which is the only way that she can say
    "How do you do?"
"Moo-moo-moo" for breakfast,
"Moo-moo-moo" for lunch;
    Melinda likes to eat her hay.
    Listen to her crunch.
"Moo-moo-moo" in the morning,
"Moo-moo-moo" at night;
    Melinda swings her long slim tail
    To left and then to right.
"Moo-moo-moo" with the sun,
"Moo-mo-moo" at the moon;
    That's a signal to the farmer
    To come and milk her soon.
"Moo-moo-moo,
Moo-moo-moo,
Moo . . . . . . oo."

Have the children chorus the "moo-moo-moo" whenever it appears in
the poem. The last "moo" is to be prolonged for the count of four or five.

TREED

Watch out, yellow pussy cat;
This is not a time to chat.
    Meow, meow, meow.
From that growly sound I hear,
I should say a dog is near.
    Meow, meow, "f, f, f!"
Must not stay to talk with me.
Climb into that apple tree.
    Mew, mew, mew.
Here, doggie, here; a bone I'll throw.
Now he's forgotten. See him go!
    Meow, meow, pssst!
A shame to give you such a fright;
His bark is much worse than his bite.
    Meow, meow, purr.

Discuss pussy cat's language. She can say "meow" in many different ways, according to how she feels.

SEWING MACHINE

"nnnnnnnnnnn" goes the sewing machine;
A coat for Neddie, a dress for Jean.
    "nnnnnnnnnnn"
The wheels hum a little tune as they race,
Putting each stitch in the proper place,
    "nnnnnnnnnnn."

Check the position of the tongue for this nasal sound which is called a continuant. The tongue rests on the little shelf behind the upper teeth. Pinch the nose together and if the sound stops, the child will know that he is making "n" correctly.

LITTLE MOSQUITO'S SONG

Little mosquito liked to sing
Up the scale and down,

      n - n

   n   n

  n   n

"n   n"
As jolly as a clown.

It made his mother angry
To hear him sing so gay,

      n - n

   n   n

  n   n

"n   n"
In such a careless way.
She said, "Beware, my darling,
For under every log . . ."

      n - n

   n   n

  n   n

"n   n"
". . . There waits a big green frog."
Little mosquito grew more careful,
And as he flew along,

"n . . . n . . . n . . ."
Went his mosquito song.

This poem provides drill on the "n" sound and on pitch discrimination. Children may prefer to have the mosquito hum a line from a well
known song instead of just humming up and down the scale.

THE COW AND THE OWL

Said the cow to the owl,
"You funny old fowl,
You sit on a bough all day.
You cannot give milk,
And you cannot say 'Moo,'
So why are you here, anyway?"
Said the owl to the cow,
"I can fly to the sky,
And say, 'Too-wit-too-whoo';
And so, Mrs. Cow,
I should like to say now,
That I'm just as important as you."
     If the owl cannot moo,
     Or the cow say "Too-whoo,"
     Then I do not see why
     They should quarrel.
          Do you?

Use for drill with the "m" and "n" sounds. Words are: *funny, cannot, anyway, important, can, and, now, milk, I'm,* and *moo.* There are two predominating vowel sounds in this poem: "ow" as in *cow, owl, fowl, bough,* and *now;* and "oo" as in *moo, whoo,* and *you.*

CHRISTMAS BELLS

I heard a bell ring far away,
Children: Ding, dong, ding, dong,
A happy bell on Christmas Day,
Children: Ding, dong, ding, dong.
Then every bell began to chime,
Children: Ding, dong, ding, dong,
To tell the world of Christmas time.
Children: Ding, dong, ding, dong.
And all the world was glad and gay,
Children: Ding, dong, ding, dong,
To see another Christmas Day.
Children: Ding, dong, ding, dong.

—Adapted (Author unknown)

ADVENTURE

As I was walking along, long, long,
I sang a gay little song, song, song.
The clock in the square said, "Bong, bong, bong."
The bell in the church said, "Dong, dong, dong."
The streetcar bell said, "Ding, ding, ding."
A bicycle horn went, "Zing, zing, zing."
The raindrops fell with a ping, ping, ping.
A bird began to sing, sing, sing
The day that I walked along, long, long,
Singing my gay little song, song, song.

Tell the children that they may help with the words that are repeated
in each line. Cue the children at each repetition by raising a finger.
Each word may be pronounced with prolonged "ng" sound. This poem
is a good vehicle for teaching phonics as other words with *ong, ing, ang,*
or *ung* endings could be added.

The teacher plays a familiar tune on the piano or phonograph while the children hum each sound, "m," "n," and "ng." They may pretend that they are tops or mosquitoes as they hum.

"mmmmmmmm" . . . lips are closed but not pressed firmly.

"nnnnnnnn" . . . tip of the tongue touches the ridge behind the upper teeth.

"ngngngngng" . . . rear of tongue touches soft palate as lips are parted.

> Feel the humming in your nose;
> That is where the humming goes.
> "m . . . m . . . m . . ."
> "n . . . n . . . n . . ."
> "ng . . . ng . . . ng . . ."

HOW MILLIE MOSQUITO LEARNED TO HUM

Ask the children to join in each time one of the mosquitoes in the story starts to sing. By the time drill on this series of sounds is given, the class will probably be well aware when it is time to participate and when it is time to listen. One of the aims of this book is to familiarize the children with the stories and poems, so that they will be able to tell or say them with a minimum of teacher assistance. This story about Millie can be dramatized with stick puppets. See instructions for making stick puppets in the section, "Devices to Use with This Book."

Millie was a baby mosquito that lived in a pond near a swamp. (*Teacher should question children as to what a swamp is.*) She was just learning to hum, but the hum was in a little, tiny voice, "nnnnnnnnnnn." She could not make her voice go up or down the scale like this: "$nn^{nn}n$." It just stayed on the same note. But Millie was only a baby mosquito and "nnnnnnn" was quite a tune for her to hum.

Millie's mother, Mrs. Mosquito, was quite a hummer herself. She hummed: "mmmmmmmm." She could hum "mmmmmmmm" for so long that you wondered how she had any breath left.

Sometimes she hummed this way: "m^{mmm}" and sometimes she hummed this way: "^{mm}mm." If she was feeling very fine she would hum this way: "$m^{mmmm}mm$." Millie could not do this, however hard she tried. It was always "nnnnnnn" on one note.

Mr. Mosquito was Millie's Daddy, and he could hum, too. It was a beautiful low hum, "ngngngngngngng." It sounded just like an organ in a church when he hummed "ngngngngngngng."

When Millie's Mother and Daddy hummed together, the duet they made was lovely. All of the mosquitoes in the swamp would stop to listen and they would all say in a chorus, "How we wish that we could hum that way!"

Often Monty, who was a naughty little boy mosquito, would tease Millie. He would fly at her with a loud "NNNNNNN" that frightened her. She would fly away as fast as she could to another part of the swamp.

One evening the moon came out, a big, round silver moon that made Millie feel as if she wanted to fly and fly. On that very evening Monty saw Millie and he rushed at her with a loud "NNNNNNN." Millie flew away as fast as her tiny wings would carry her and soon she had flown right out of the swamp. She knew that she was in a meadow and not the swamp because she could smell the new-mown hay and the wild flowers.

Suddenly she saw a light, and as insects like to do, Millie flew toward it. As she flew closer, she saw that the light was coming through the window of a house. She glided up to the window sill and peeked in. Then she heard something. It was a sweet humming sound. If you could hear snowflakes falling or dewdrops dripping or tiny bells chiming miles away, then you would know what the sweet sound was like.

There in a crib was a baby boy holding a snoozy puppy. The baby boy was humming his puppy to sleep.

"Oh," whispered Millie. "That is the song that I want to learn. Maybe if I stay here to listen awhile, I can sing it just like the baby boy."

"$m^{mm^{mm}m}mm \ldots m^{mm^{mm}m}mm$," hummed the little boy. But soon the song stopped, for the baby boy was asleep.

"If I can only remember that lovely tune," sighed Millie. "I will try to hum it right now . . . '$n^{nn^{n}n}nn$' . . . Oh, I do remember it." And she hurried back to the swamp, humming her song all the way home . . . "$n^{nn^{nn}n}nn \ldots n^{nn^{nn}n}nn \ldots n^{nn^{nn}n}nn$."

Mother and Daddy Mosquito heard the tune as Millie neared the swamp. "Who is humming so beautifully?" they asked. All of the other mosquitoes asked the same question, and they flew about trying to find the mysterious singer.

No one ever suspected that it was Millie. You will remember that at the beginning of the story she could hum only on one note: "nnnnnnn."

Finally, Daddy Mosquito heard the song coming from under a leaf. So quietly it came that he could scarcely hear it. He looked under the leaf, and there was Millie, humming very softly, for she was almost asleep.

"$n^{nn^{nnn}n}n$," hummed Millie.

"$m^{mm^{mmm}m}m$," hummed Mother Mosquito.

"$ng^{ng^{ng}ng}ngngng$," hummed Daddy Mosquito.

Monty, the naughty mosquito, said not a word, and all of the mosquitoes listened and listened. They wondered how Millie had learned to sing such a beautiful song, but so far as I know, Millie never told her secret to anyone.

That means that just you and I know her secret, and I am not going to tell. I don't believe that you will either.

FINGER PLAY

Finger play is one of the simplest forms of dramatic projection. It appeals to the imagination of children who enjoy playing "let's pretend." The child, when holding up or bending down a finger in response to the poem, identifies himself, his hands, and his fingers with squirrels, puppies, wash day, or knives and forks, whatever the game may dictate.

Even the ten-months-old baby gains pleasure from a game of "This little pig went to market." Pre-school and kindergarten children take delight in exercising their powers of imagery as they convert their fingers into "mother's looking glass" or "baby's cradle." The attention span of the immature child is extended, for he will listen attentively to see what the squirrel or puppy in the poem will do next. Finger play becomes a technique for bringing the timid, shy, or unresponsive child more actively into classroom participation without causing him to feel singled out. And the joy of participation is increased when a child learns the lines so that he can recite them himself while making his hands and fingers help tell the story.

Finger play lends itself to the "classroom approach" in speech correction. Many of the lines of the poem or story begin with the same word. This repetition serves to establish a pattern for a sound used in the initial, medial, or final position. For example, the poems "Five Little Squirrels" and "Squirrels in a Tree" provide repetition of the voiced "th" sound in *this,* the "l" sound in *little,* and the "skw" blend in *squirrel.* The "d" substitution for voiced "th" or a faulty "s" will be corrected sooner if a child learns to produce the correct sound through the repetitious wording of a poem or story which gives pleasure and which is a part of the group learning process.

The magic flannel board may be used as a visual aid, with animals or objects placed on the board and taken down as the finger play poem may direct.

Number drill is also a part of finger play. Children learn to add and subtract by chorusing the poem again and again. When one snowman melts in the poem" Ten Little Snowmen," they will automatically say, "Then there were nine." Finger play permits much correct repeating of numbers containing sounds which present difficulty, such as "th" in three, "f" in four and five, "r" in three and four, and "s" in six and seven.

The authors use finger play as a definite part of the classroom speech improvement lessons, for they serve as an excellent step to other speech activities. They help relieve physical tensions. They promote cooperation and aid in establishing group readiness.

TEN LITTLE CHICKS

Ten little chicks sat under a vine.
One flew away, and then there were nine.
Nine little chicks cried, "Wait, wait, wait."
One went to get a drink, and then there were eight.
Eight little chicks in a line so even;
One ran to get some corn, and then there were seven.
Seven little chicks said, "We're in a dreadful fix."
One said, "I'm leaving, too," and then there were six.
Six little chicks were glad to be alive.
One chased a doodle bug, and then there were five.
Five little chicks were resting on the floor.
One saw the farmer, and then there were four.
Four little chicks sighed, "Oh, dear me."
One went to roost, and then there were three.
Three little chicks grew, and grew, and grew.
One became a rooster, and then there were two.
Two little chicks said, "We won't run."
One changed his mind, and then there was one.
One little chick said, "This is no fun."
So he grew up . . . and then there was none.

Children will enjoy placing the ten chicks on the flannel board and
taking them off one by one as the poem is recited. Finger ring puppets
may also be used. See the section on "Devices to Use with This Book"
for instructions. The hands are held up with fingers extended. Bend the
fingers down one at a time as each chick goes away.

FIVE RED PEGS

Five red pegs standing in a row;
Watch out, watch out, here they go.
Down goes one peg,
Down go two pegs,
Down go three pegs,
Down go four pegs,
Down go five pegs;
All five pegs
Lying just so.

Let the fingers follow the action of the poem as it is recited.

FIVE LITTLE KITTENS*

Five furry kittens
Waiting in the house;
Softly, softly,
They think they hear a mouse.
The white kitten says, "Be still."
The gray kitten says, "We will."
The brown kitten says, "Oh, where?"
The striped kitten says, "Take care."
The black kitten says, "Right there."
"Squeak," went the mouse,
And they all ran under the house.

Choose five children to be the kittens and say what each kitten says. Have them hold up kitten pictures which they have colored. The rest of the class may participate by holding up one hand with fingers extended and grasping the fingers one at a time with the other hand as each kitten speaks. The fingers make running movements on the last line.

---

* Used by special permission of *The Grade Teacher*

FIVE LITTLE VALENTINES

One little valentine said, "I love you."
Tommy made another; then there were two.
Two little valentines, one for me;
Mary made another; then there were three.
Three little valentines said, "We need one more."
Johnny made another; then there were four.
Four little valentines, one more to arrive;
Susan made another; then there were five.
Five little valentines all ready to say,
"Be my valentine on this happy day."

Let the class make valentines. Five children are chosen to hold up
their valentines one by one as the poem is said. Substitute the names of the
children chosen. All five may say the last line. Each other child in the class
holds up a closed fist and extends a finger when another valentine is added.

SLEEPY PUPPIES

Five little puppies playing on the floor.
One crept to bed; then there were four.
Four sleepy puppies were as tired as could be.
One curled up in a ball; then there were three.
Three sleepy puppies said, "We are drowsy, too."
One found a blanket; then there were two.
Two sleepy puppies too tired to run;
One lay upon the grass; then there was one.
One sleepy puppy said, "Night has begun."
He found a kennel; then there was none.

Have the class perform these activities as the poem is said:
Line   2—Fingers simulate walking movements.
Line   4—Make a circle with the arms.
Line   6—Simulate pulling a blanket up under the chin.
Line   8—Both hands extended, palms down.
Line 10—Finger tips together to form pointed kennel roof.

FIVE LITTLE PILGRIMS

Five little Pilgrims on Thanksgiving Day:
The first one said, "I'll have cake if I may."
The second one said, "I'll have turkey, roasted."
The third one said, "I'll have chestnuts, toasted."
The fourth one said, "I'll have pumpkin pie."
The fifth one said, "Oh, cranberries I spy."
But before they ate any turkey or dressing,
All of the Pilgrims said a Thanksgiving blessing.

Finger ring Pilgrim heads may be used with this poem. See the section on "Devices to Use with This Book" for instructions for making. The hands should come together as in prayer on the last two lines.

SQUIRRELS IN A TREE

Five little squirrels sitting in a tree:
This little squirrel said, "These nuts are for me."
This little squirrel said, "I like to eat."
This little squirrel said, "Nuts are a treat."
This little squirrel said, "Do you want some?"
This little squirrel said, "You may have one."
Five little squirrels went bob, bob, bob.
(Bend fingers)
Five little squirrels went nod, nod, nod.
(Bend wrists)
Five little squirrels went patter, patter, patter.
(Wiggle fingers)
Five little squirrels went chatter, chatter, chatter.
(Clap hands)
Five little squirrels scolded you and me
As they sat and ate nuts in the big tall tree.

This finger play game is excellent for drill on the voiced "th" sound and the *sq* blend ("skw").

226

TEN LITTLE SNOWMEN

Ten little snowmen dressed up fine;

This one melted, and then there were nine.

    Nine little snowmen standing tall and straight;

    This one melted, and then there were eight.

Eight little snowmen white as clouds in heaven;

This one melted, and then there were seven.

    Seven little snowmen with arms made of sticks;

    This one melted, and then there were six.

Six little snowmen looking so alive;

This one melted, and then there were five.

    Five little snowmen with mittens from the store;

    This one melted, and then there were four.

Four little snowmen beneath a green pine tree;

This one melted, and then there were three.

    Three little snowmen with pipes and mufflers, too;

    This one melted, and then there were two.

Two little snowmen standing in the sun;

This one melted, and then there was one.

    One little snowman started to run,

    But he melted away, and then there was none.

This poem can be used for relaxation. As each of the snowmen melts, the teacher should point to one or more children who are to sink to the floor in a relaxed manner. For finger play, have the children count off the snowmen on their fingers.

TEN LITTLE COOKIES

Ten little cookies, brown and crisp and fine;
Mama gave Baby one; then there were nine.
Nine little cookies on a china plate;
Betty took a small one; then there were eight.
Eight little cookies in a row so even;
Daddy ate the biggest one; then there were seven.
Seven little cookies; some very hungry chicks
Ate a little tiny one; then there were six.
Six little cookies; when Mama went to drive,
Betty ate another; then there were five.
Five little cookies; a mouse came through the door,
Took a little nibble; then there were four.
Four little cookies waiting there for tea;
Baby took a brown one; then there were three.
Three little cookies; Mama said, "I, too,
Would like a very little one"; then there were two.
Two little cookies; see the mousie run
To take another nibble; then there was one.
One little cookie; the story is almost done.
Baby ate the last one; then there was none.

The hands should be held up with fingers extended. A finger is bent down each time there is one cookie less.

THESE ARE MOTHER'S KNIVES AND FORKS

These are mother's knives and forks;
This is mother's table.
This is mother's looking glass;
And this is baby's cradle.

For knives and forks: All fingers are held straight up; for the table: lock the fingers and hold the hands in a horizontal position; for the looking glass: one hand is held up, palm toward the face; for the cradle: lock the fingers, cup the hands, and swing them back and forth.

THIS IS THE WAY WE WASH OUR CLOTHES*

This is the way we wash our clothes,
Wash our clothes, wash our clothes.
This is the way we wash our clothes
So early Monday morning.

This is the way we iron our clothes,
Iron our clothes, iron our clothes.
This is the way we iron our clothes
So early Tuesday morning.

This is the way we mend our shoes,
Mend our shoes, mend our shoes.
This is the way we mend our shoes
So early Wednesday morning.

This is the way we sweep the house,
Sweep the house, sweep the house.
This is the way we sweep the house
So early Thursday morning.

This is the way we stir a cake,
Stir a cake, stir a cake.
This is the way we stir a cake
So early Saturday morning.

—Anonymous

This is not only a good action poem for teaching days of the week, but is also a means for getting drill on the "s" in *this, sweep, stir,* and *house.* The "sh" in *wash* and *shoes* and the "r" in *iron* and *stir* are important repetitions for those children who need to improve these sounds.

* *The University Book Shelf,* University Society, New York.

EASTER RABBITS

Solo: Five little Easter rabbits
        Sitting at the door;
    One hopped away;
        Then there were four.

Children: Hop, hop, hop, hop,
        See how they run;
    Hop, hop, hop, hop,
        They think it great fun.

Solo: Four little Easter rabbits
        Sitting under a tree;
    One hopped away;
        Then there were three.

Children: *(Repeat refrain)*

Solo: Three little Easter rabbits
        Looking at you;
    One hopped away;
        Then there were two.

Children: *(Repeat refrain)*

Solo: Two little Easter rabbits
        Sitting in the sun;
    One hopped away;
        Then there was one.

Children: (*Repeat refrain*)
Solo: One little Easter rabbit
             Left all alone;
         He hopped away;
             Then there was none.
Children: Hop, hop, hop, hop,
             All gone away;
         Hop, hop, hop, hop,
             They'll come back some day.

                               —*Anonymous*

Rabbit finger ring puppets can be used. Let the children take turns in putting the puppets on their fingers and taking them off. The children not using the puppets may clap on the refrain.

THIS LITTLE COW

This little cow eats grass;
This little cow eats hay;
This little cow drinks water;
And this little cow runs away.
This little cow does nothing
But just lie down all day.

                       —MOTHER GOOSE

One hand is held up with the fingers bent to make a fist. The fingers are extended one at a time as each cow is mentioned. Let the thumb be last, and when lines 5 and 6 are said, make the thumb wag back and forth and then stay bent in order to "just lie down all day."

FIVE LITTLE SQUIRRELS*

Five little squirrels sat up in a tree.
This little squirrel said, "What do I see?"
This little squirrel said, "I smell a gun."
This little squirrel said, "Let's run. Let's run."
This little squirrel said, "Let's hide in the shade."
This little squirrel said, "I'm not afraid."
Bang! went the gun.
And away they all ran, every one.

—Anonymous

One hand is held up with fingers extended. The other hand touches the extended fingers one at a time as the squirrels are counted off. The hands are clapped together when the gun goes "bang." The fingers make running movements on the last line.

HERE'S A LITTLE WASH BENCH*

Here's a little wash bench;

> *(Hands extended, palms down;
> first together, then move apart.)*

Here's a little tub;

> *(Hands and fingers rounded to
> form a small circle.)*

Here's a little scrubbing board;

> *(Hands extended about a foot
> apart; palms face inward.)*

And here's the way to rub.

> *(Hands perform scrubbing
> motions.)*

---

* *The University Book Shelf,* University Society, New York.

Here's a little cake of soap;

> *(Fingers of one hand bent to form circle.)*

Here's a dipper new;

> *(Other hand cupped, palm up.)*

Here's the basket wide and deep;

> *(Arms form horizontal circle.)*

And here are clothespins two.

> *(Index and middle fingers of both hands crossed and held up.)*

Here's the line, away up high;

> *(Hands grasp imaginary line overhead.)*

Here the clothes are flying;

> *(Hands swing back and forth to resemble flopping clothes.)*

Here's the sun so warm and bright;

> *(Arms form circle overhead.)*

And here the clothes are drying.

> *(Hands extended, palms face frontwards.)*

> —*Anonymous*

THIS IS THE WAY MY FINGERS STAND*

This is the way my fingers stand,
    Fingers stand, fingers stand.
        This is the way my fingers stand
        So early in the morning.

This is the way I fold my hands,
    Fold my hands, fold my hands.
        This is the way I fold my hands
        So early in the morning.

This is the way they go to rest,
    Go to rest, go to rest.
        This is the way they go to rest
        So early in the morning.

—Anonymous

This poem, which can also be used as a readiness device, may be sung to the tune of "Here We Go Round the Mulberry Bush." When the fingers "go to rest," they are placed on the desk or in the lap while the child drops his head forward.

* *The University Book Shelf,* University Society, New York.

SAID THIS LITTLE FAIRY

Said this little fairy, "I'm as tired as can be."
Said this little fairy, "My eyes can hardly see."
Said this little fairy, "I'd like to go to bed."
Said this little fairy, "To rest my weary head."
Said this little fairy, "Come, climb the stairs with me."
One, two, three, four, five they tip-toed
Just as still as still could be.

One hand is held up with fingers extended. The index finger of the other hand touches the extended fingers one at a time as the fairies speak. The repetition of the word *said* provides drill for the "s" sound and the exercise can be used for relaxation.

PUTTING FINGERS TO SLEEP

Sleepy little fingers
Lying in my lap;
First, you, Baby Finger,
Time you took a nap.
Now, Ring Finger, hurry!
Middle Finger, too!
Pointer Finger, bend your head;
It is time for you.
Who is this so wide awake;
Just like a little wiggle snake?
Sh ... sh ... Thumb, don't make a peep.
See? All my fingers are asleep.

Bend down extended fingers one at a time as they are mentioned in the poem.

PART III

GUIDE TO PHONETIC SYMBOLS

Phonetics and *phonics* are terms which are often confused as to meaning. *Phonetics* is the science of speech sounds in actual use—a system of spelling in which each symbol or letter always represents the same spoken sound. *Phonics* is the application of phonetics to the teaching of reading. It deals not only with the spoken sound, but with the letters of the alphabet. It is an aid to word recognition.

The phonetic alphabet makes it possible for a teacher to recognize speech errors or deviations through the awareness of sounds, regardless of how the sound may be spelled. For example, the sound "s" may be spelled as follows: *s* in *bus*, *ss* in *kiss*, *sc* in *scene*, *se* in *vase*, *ce* in *face*, *ps* in *psalm*, *st* in *listen*, *sch* in *schism*, *x* in *six*, *sw* in *answer*, or *c* in *city*. The letter is silent in *island*, and *corps*. Likewise, one letter may represent several sounds, each one involving the speech helpers in a different position. There is no phonetic similarity among the sounds of *a* in *ate*, *am*, *all*, *above*, and *far*.

In the phonetic alphabet, however, there is only one symbol for each sound, and only one sound for each symbol, representing a particular adjustment of the speech mechanism which may involve teeth, tongue, lips, soft palate, and vocal cords.

There are only twenty-six letters in the English alphabet, but there are approximately fifty different sounds in the English language. The phonetic alphabet makes use of sixteen of the letters of the English alphabet to represent the same sounds that they usually stand for in spelled words plus the additional consonant symbols listed in the chart below.

A knowledge of the relationship between these phonetic symbols which represent sounds and the actual spelling of words enables a teacher to avoid confusing sounds with letters. The spelling of a word may not reveal the sound at all, i. e., *enough, right, raced, nation.* Sounds are heard, but letters are seen.

The following chart lists only the consonant sounds discussed in this book. The complete phonetic alphabet is not included because the vowel sounds are not commonly misarticulated, and such additional explanations as would be necessary might confuse rather than help a teacher trying to carry out a program of classroom speech improvement on the primary level.

Voiceless	*Voiced*
s — *s*ee	z — *z*oo
p — *p*et	b — *b*aby
t — *t*o	d — *d*o

k – *k*itten　　　　g – *g*o

f – *f*un　　　　　v – *v*ine

θ – *th*ree　　　　ð – *th*e

ʃ – *sh*e　　　　　ʒ – trea*s*ure

tʃ – *ch*air　　　dʒ – *j*ump

hw – *wh*at　　　w – *w*e

h – *h*e

r – *r*un, g*ir*l, fath*er*

l – *l*et

j – *y*ou

m – *m*e

n – *n*o

ŋ – si*ng*

ALPHABETICAL INDEX
OF MATERIALS

240

INDEX FOR UNIT INTEGRATION

243

244

11 12 13 14 15 16 17 18 19 20 21 22 23 24 25 — K — 70 69 68 67 66 65 64 63 62 61